They Will Know
They Are Loved

A Family's Life with Premature Twins

JON WESTBY

Kirk House Publishers
Minneapolis, Minnesota

They Will Know They Are Loved:
A Family's Life with Premature Twins
Author: Jon Westby
Editor: Sandra J. Westby

Cover Design: Glen Broich
Cover Photo: Sandy Houts
All other photos from family collection
Photo Scanning and Enhancement: Abby Baker

Library of Congress Cataloging-in-Publication Data
Westby, Jon.
    They will know they are loved : a family's life with premature
twins / by Jon Westby.
        p. cm.
    ISBN 1-886513-61-9 (alk. paper)
        1. Infants (Premature). 2. Infants (Premature)—Family
relationships. 3. Twins—Family relationships. 4. Birth weight,
Low—Complications. 5. Multiple birth. 6. Child rearing. I. Title.

RJ250 .W476 2003
618.92'011'019—dc21

                                                    2002192465

Kirk House Publishers, PO Box 390759, Minneapolis, MN 55439
Manufactured in the United States of America

Dedication

I dedicate this book to my loving wife and best friend Catherine. I hope by writing this book I can in some small way repay her for all the love and support she has given my sons and me.

Acknowledgements

The following people contributed to the publication of this book by providing encouragement, medical information, and technical expertise:

Abby Baker, Glen Broich, H.J. Cummins, Dr. Michael Georgieff, Tom Green, Sandy Houts, Kari Joiner, Mary Kenyon, Mary Jo Kirschbaum, Mary Lathrop, Marla Mills, Jim and Dinah Patrykus, Mark Trumper, Jenny Wandersee, Kathryn Warner, Lynette Wayne, Herman and Susan Weinlick, Dick and Sandra Westby, Carol Witte.

Table of Contents

Forward

by Dr. Michael Georgieff

It is my distinct honor and privilege to write the introduction for this unique book. I consider myself extremely fortunate to have been James' and Henry's doctor, not only in the Newborn Intensive Care Unit, but also in the NICU Follow-up Program. James and Henry are truly remarkable characters, not so much in what they overcame medically, but in what they taught their parents, nurses, and doctors about the gift of life.

As a physician who researches the remarkable plasticity of the human brain, I am perpetually amazed by the fact that babies born as gestationally immature as these two boys can turn into the joyful, rambunctious elementary-schoolers that they are. To think that their brains, at birth, were as smooth as cue balls; and despite the fact that they lived in the environment that they normally would have (i.e. their mother's womb) for only 26 weeks, they steadfastly and stubbornly grew and developed into the wonderful children that Jon describes.

But that is not the most unique aspect of this book. Many books have been written about "miracle" premature infants who survive against all odds. No, the reason this book is remarkable is because it is written from the perspective of a loving father who, perhaps, underwent an even greater transformation than his infant sons. From the first chapter of this book, I was riveted by Jon's struggles and by the evolution of his insights into the commitments of marriage and fatherhood. The role of the father in the life of critically-ill infants has rarely been considered. My experience with NICU dads has been that they are frequently shunted to the side as peripheral players by the medical team. Sometimes they abandon their relationship with the mother and are slowly marginalized out of their marital relationship. The divorce rate among couples with infants who were in the NICU is dramatically increased.

Jon's remarkable insight into what was happening— not only to his infants and his wife, but to himself and his relationships with his loved ones— makes this book a most satisfying read. We all can learn so much about what makes a family whole, even if we do not see our children at the brink of death.

This book has changed what I tell parents, and especially fathers, to expect about their NICU experience and the long, unfolding story in the follow-up period after their infants are home. It is a book about hope and reality: a chance for all of us, but especially fathers, to consider what our relationships with our children and our loved ones are based on.

Dr. Michael Georgieff is a Professor of Pediatrics at the University of Minnesota where he also co-directs the Center for Neuro-Behavioral Development. He serves as Director of the Neonatal Intensive Care Unit Follow-up Clinic at Fairview-University Medical Center. He has done extensive research in the areas of nutrition, iron deficiencies, and neonatal outcomes. He lives with his wife and three children in St. Paul, Minnesota.

THEY WILL KNOW THEY ARE LOVED

Author's Notes

In January of 2001, I sat at my computer at school with the intention of writing down a couple of thoughts I wanted to share with my wife Catherine— thoughts regarding our being parents of five-year-old twin boys. Seven months, one hundred-fifteen pages, and dozens of run-on sentences later, I surprised her with a loosely-organized manuscript (which I called a book) entitled *Henry and James: The Miracle of Life.* It was my present to her for our 12th wedding anniversary.

After Catherine had time to read the book several times, she asked a few family members and close friends to read it. They encouraged us to share the story with a larger audience. We let the manuscript sit on the shelf for five months. Then in February of 2002, I decided to begin reworking the book for publication.

I first enlisted the help of my mother, a retired high school English teacher. She became my editor— correcting grammar and punctuation, rearranging text, challenging me and reminding me of lost memories. As I continued to write and rewrite, my mother began the process of putting some structure and order into my meandering thoughts and words.

As I learned more about the publishing business, I realized we would need more help. My college roomate, Glen Broich, a graphic designer, agreed to design the cover. A close friend, Abby Baker, also a graphic designer, volunteered to format the photograph pages. Our dear friend, Sandy Houts, a professional photographer, took the cover photos. Dr. Michael Georgieff, one of Henry's and James' NICU doctors, graciously agreed not only to help edit the technical matter but also to write a forward for the book. I phoned other friends asking them to proofread copy or to give advice about printing and about starting a business.

The writing of this book took on a life of its own. It was truly a labor of love. If not for the help of many devoted individuals, it would have never come to be. I need to thank all those involved with getting this book to press.

JDW

Introduction

My wife Catherine deserves most, if not all, of the credit for the love and nurturing that takes place in our family. It is she who has held up the foundation of our family. I have learned so much from her and from our sons that I could never repay them. I am not the greatest communicator in the world; more often than not, I cannot find the words to express my feelings and gratitude. Silence is a friend of mine. I hope that by writing this story I connect with Catherine; and that, after reading this for the first time, she can understand some of the feelings, memories, and thoughts I have neglected to tell her over these past five years.

I have witnessed the miracle of life. I have now experienced parenthood for the first time and I cannot believe how it has affected me. I get to laugh, cuddle, hold, cry, worry; and it is OK. The unconditional love that our own children give us is the greatest feeling I've ever experienced. Those of you who are parents know what I'm writing about; it is an unexplainable feeling or bond we have with our children, and I get to experience it two-fold. We have twins.

13

Catherine and I are fortunate. Our sons were born prematurely; and if not for the prayers of many people, the love of family, and the wonder of modern-day medicine, all might have been lost. But by some miracle, our boys were spared. Over these past five years I have watched in wonder as my sons have grown and developed. They continually amaze me.

I am a very proud father.

CHAPTER 1

Running from Responsibility

November 29, 1995

My mind is racing. The questions keep coming. I cannot find the answers. *They're too small; how can they survive? What if one makes it but not the other? How will Catherine handle it if they both die?*

Sweat soaks my clothes. A sudden chill travels down my back on this cold blustery morning. I check my heart rate monitor as I run across the Ford Bridge and head into Minneapolis along West River Road— 155 beats per minute. I should be turning around and heading back home. I've been running for 40 minutes. I have no water to replenish my increasing thirst. Turning around would be the smart and responsible thing to do . . . I push forward.

By the time I get to Lake Street, my endorphins have kicked in and my mind is in overdrive. I am lost in my own thoughts. *Where do they get their strength?*

Where do they get their courage to keep fighting? What kinds of disabilities will they face if they do survive? I check my watch once again and realize I've been out for over an hour. Reluctantly, I turn back for home. The wind I have been fighting gives me a sudden boost and sends me on my way. My pace quickens; my heart rate has reached 160. I climb the hill to the Franklin Avenue Bridge. Now the questions come faster. *What crises will we have to face today? Will we have to care for them when they reach adulthood?* I am running faster; my heart rate monitor reads 167. My muscles show their first sign of fatigue as my calves start a slow burn.

I force myself to think of something else. My mind backtracks to the previous summer when my wife Catherine and I vacationed out west. I remember watching the fog slowly roll over the High Divide as I backpacked in the Olympic Peninsula. We walked barefoot, hand in hand, along the beautiful sandy beaches of the Oregon coast. Catherine was carrying our expected child. Can it be that this was all only four months ago?

As I take the turn and start heading up Summit Avenue past the University of St. Thomas, my body starts its slow breakdown from fatigue and dehydration. My heart is thumping along at a steady 170 beats per minute. I suddenly become irrational; I'm making no sense at all. I have convinced myself that if I run fast—faster than I have ever run—everything will be

OK and my questions will be answered.

I take the last turn for home down Edgecumbe Boulevard; my monitor reads 177. I'm racing and I know it is only a matter of blocks before I reach my front steps. It's harder to breathe and I have developed an aching stitch in my side. My eyes begin to water. I tell myself it is due to the salty sweat pouring into them. As I reach the corner of my block one last question enters my quivering mind: *Do they even know that we love them?*

I stumble up our front steps, holding my side, gasping for air. I have been running for two hours. I make my way around to the back door and let myself into our empty house. In the middle of the living room I collapse in a heap onto the hardwood floor.

CHAPTER 2

Henry Jon and James David

October 19,1995

In Catherine's fifth month of pregnancy her doctor ordered an ultrasound because her uterus was larger than normal for a single pregnancy at that stage. During the preliminary examination Dr. Williams, Catherine's obstetrician, asked us if there was any history of twins in our family. Five minutes later the ultrasound technician asked the same question. Our response to each was a definite "No!"

The technician then cracked us up by asking Catherine, "Are you going to punch me if this ultrasound shows twins?" At that point, even after being asked twice, I had absolutely no thought of having twins.

A nurse prepped Catherine for her ultrasound. The technician had her lie down in what looked like a dentist chair. I sat on a tall stool next to her. The tech gooped up my wife's abdomen with a vaseline-type substance, then picked up a wand-like instrument called a *transducer* which she gently placed on Catherine's pregnant belly. The tech proceeded to turn knobs and dials on the ultrasound machine. It wasn't long before we saw on the monitor the outline of a tiny baby with delicate features. The image was crystal clear; we could easily make out all the features: head, arms, legs, even fingers.

The technician kept moving the wand around Catherine's abdomen. Within a few seconds of our seeing the first baby, a very clear outline of a second baby appeared on the monitor. Before the technician could say anything, Catherine sat up; I jumped up, pointed at the monitor, and very excitedly—or fearfully—said, "There's two of them on there!"

The technician and the nurse both laughed and said, "Yes, you're right! You're having twins!" Catherine and I looked at each other. Our ear-to-ear grins quickly changed to laughter. Our lives at that moment had dramatically changed, and neither of us knew what to say.

At this point Dr. Williams rejoined us and asked if we wanted to know the sex of the twins. We had both agreed earlier in the pregnancy that we did not want to know the sex of our baby; but now, facing the prospect of having twins, we waffled and agreed it might be a good idea to know ahead of time. The doctor and the technician worked together, both handling the transducer to get the best look at the first baby, and they both came to the same conclusion. It was a boy. They repeated the process with the other baby and again agreed—another boy. We were going to have twin boys. WOW!

Next the doctor and the technician tried to determine whether these boys were identical or fraternal twins. They were checking to see whether each boy had his own placenta indicating fraternal twins, or whether they shared one placenta as identical twins do. The doctor's conclusion was that we were going to have identical twin boys.

For the rest of that day, I was in such an excited and frightened state of mind, I didn't know what to do with myself. Catherine suggested we go home and begin the process of informing our family and friends. In the car she reminded me that I was the one who kept saying, "There is no way we are having twins!" right up to the very moment we saw the second baby on the ultrasound screen.

We called our parents first. Catherine's mother let loose with a loud scream of excitement when she got the news over the phone that she'd have twin grandsons. She was standing in the lobby of the State Capitol Building.

When friends of ours have announced a single-child pregnancy, I've generally made some polite comment such as "Oh, I'm so happy for you," or "How are you feeling?" or " Have you picked out a name?"

But when we announced the impending birth of twins, there was no subtlety; we got responses like "Oh, wow!" or "Is your house big enough?" or "Are you going to buy diapers by the truckload?" From most of my buddies, I got exuberant laughter.

I received a call from one of my closest friends who has two young sons. "Yeah, Westby," he said, "I just got off the phone with Halbert (another buddy with two young sons); and we laughed our asses off for ten minutes." He added, "We both decided— better you than us!" That was my friends' way of telling us, "Congratulations!"

To say Catherine and I were now excited would be an understatement. We were ecstatic. We began researching, reading anything we could find about twins: delivery of twins, parenting twins, naming twins. From our college health texts and Catherine's pregnancy books, we began to understand how this could have happened to us.

Identical twins are conceived when one egg is fertilized by one sperm. This egg then divides, resulting in two developing babies with the same inherited characteristics. The division usually occurs after the egg has become implanted in the uterus. Identical twins usually have their own cords and bags of water, but they share a placenta.

Fraternal twins are conceived when the woman releases two eggs, which are then fertilized independently by two separate sperm. These two eggs then implant and develop separately in the uterus.

Early on in Catherine's pregnancy we had chosen one boy's name and were working on a girl's name. We had already decided to name a boy *Henry James* in honor of two important men in our families. My grandfather, Henry Olaf Westby, was 85 years old at the time. I think of Grandpa Hank as a great Norwegian: loving, hard-working, strong, proud, stoic, humble, and short on conversation. The middle name *James* came from Catherine's father, James Patrykus. A caring father of three, he is humble, well-educated, spiritual, and a very hard worker. Unlike Grandpa Hank, he finds conversation easy.

When we realized we had to come up with an additional boy's name, we laughed and said, "Well, we could pick another name out of a book." But we did not think this would go over well with our one son when we would later tell them: "You, Henry, are named in honor of your great-grandfather and your grandfather; and Billy, we pulled your name out of a book." We solved the problem by dividing the name *Henry James* and giving each of our sons one of these well-chosen names. We also gave each boy one of my two names as his middle name. I hope my twin boys, Henry Jon and James David, wear their names with honor.

CHAPTER 3

Holding On

October 29, 1995

Catherine thought something might be up when she just didn't feel quite right. Call it a mother's intuition. She was experiencing lower back pain, and she knew this was not supposed to be happening now in her fifth month of pregnancy. On her way back into town after judging a speech tournament, Catherine decided to see her obstetrician. Her idea was to get some reassurance from her doctor. He would tell her what was wrong and what measures to take and then send her home. She was wrong. Catherine would not see our house again until after the boys were born. The quick trip to her doctor turned into one month of bed rest in the hospital.

Catherine went directly to the triage center at the hospital; a nurse checked her and found that she had dilated to three centimeters. Catherine was just 22 weeks into her pregnancy. At this stage, a dilation of three to four centimeters is a cause for concern because it often brings on premature delivery. Catherine was immediately checked into the hospital and placed on bed rest.

I learned from our telephone answering machine that my wife was in the hospital. I had been in Duluth for the annual Minnesota High School Hockey Coaches' Conference. When I got home I checked our machine; there were four different messages from Catherine. Her first one said, "Hi, honey. Just to let you know I'm stopping by the hospital for a quick check up, and then I'll be right home." I listened to her cheery voice, expecting her to walk in the door soon. To my surprise, there were three more messages, all from Catherine— each one getting progressively more serious. In the last one she said, "Honey, I've been checked into the hospital on bed rest. I need you to call me and then get up here with my toothbrush and some warm pajamas." Now she sounded worried! But I was more confused than concerned about the situation.

When I reached her hospital room by phone, Catherine informed me that she was lying in the *Trendelenburg* position—on her back with her hips elevated. She explained that this position would release any unneeded pressure on the cervix due to gravity. Basically, the doctors asked Catherine to "stand on her head" for an extended period of time so that the babies couldn't fall out.

I rounded up my wife's essentials and drove to the hospital. Catherine burst into tears as I walked into her room. After carrying these babies for 22 weeks, she was terrified of losing them. I was of little help in comforting her.

Soon the doctor came in and explained the gravity of the situation. Catherine needed to be on extended bed rest, possibly for one to three months; and the babies needed close monitoring. The doctor also explained that he would have to perform a procedure called a *cerclage*, which involved sewing up Catherine's cervix to prevent her from dilating further. Done under anesthesia, the procedure is considered fairly dangerous to the pregnancy because any manipulation of the cervix can cause preterm labor. Dr. Williams performed Catherine's cerclage the following day in the operating room.

All I could think about was how quickly things had changed. Two days before, when I had left town, Catherine was busy at work, happily daydreaming about what cute new outfits she could buy the boys while I was gone. It was just ten days earlier that we first found out we were having twins.

Catherine looks back on that day and remembers being initially calm about her impending bed rest— not truly understanding the seriousness of her situation. While waiting in the triage area, she had asked her nurse where the bathroom was. Nurse Kay smiled, gently put a hand on Catherine's arm, and said, "Oh honey, I don't think you understand. You won't be getting up to use the bathroom for quite awhile." It was only then that Catherine started to feel some anxiety.

The following month was trying for both of us. After observing my wife's extended bed rest, I have much more empathy and understanding for couples I meet who have gone through the same ordeal. We experienced differences emotionally and physically during these four weeks. Catherine's job was to relax, be patient, follow doctors' orders, and hopefully let these babies grow. She couldn't get up, couldn't go anywhere or have any independence. She was at the mercy of her nurses and doctors, coming in at all hours to take blood pressures, hook up heart rate monitors, deliver medications.

Catherine established a daily routine. She spent the early morning hours praying to hold onto her babies. Then it was breakfast time and nurse's check-up time. A little later Catherine conferred with the doctor, then spent the remainder of the morning reading a magazine or watching television. Afternoons she talked with friends on the phone or in person, and tried to catch a little nap. We spent the evenings together, between nurses' visits. I am amazed to this day at the patience Catherine showed through this entire month of bed rest.

While Catherine's job was to stay in bed and try to relax, my days were filled with activity. After teaching elementary school physical education, I dashed to a local high school to catch a school bus which transported the hockey team to the ice arena, coached hockey, bussed back to the high school, hustled up to the hospital to see my wife, gained the day's information on her condition, and finally drove home to sleep. Five days a week. Physically, it was a tough month, but it did prepare me for the schedule I'd have to keep after the boys were born. It just became a way of life for me for nearly seven months: work, coach, hospital, and home—in that order. Throughout these weeks I was still not very worried; I was convinced Catherine and our boys were going to be OK.

More than once in her month of bed rest Catherine started to go into premature labor. Twice she called me at the ice rink. She cried, "Jon, I'm having contractions! The doctor thinks you should come to the hospital." She was scared out of her mind that she was about to lose our babies. But by the time I got to the hospital, the contractions had stopped and Catherine was calmer. Everything was fine for the time being.

These false alarms were especially draining on her. It was difficult physically: having the contractions of premature labor, fighting to keep the boys, being strongly medicated. But it was also difficult emotionally. Catherine knew she must hold on—that birth at this early time would mean almost certain death for our babies. I can only imagine what she went through. Even though I kept a grueling schedule that month, Catherine—being confined to the hospital—had the tougher job.

From a medical standpoint, we learned a great deal. Catherine was almost constantly hooked up to a *fetal heart rate monitor.* She had two elastic bands around her abdomen, one for each baby. These bands needed constant adjusting. When one of the boys would move, the monitor would lose track of the baby's heartbeat. We shared a few good laughs with the nurses as they would futilely try to adjust the elastic straps, attempting to pick up the boys' heartbeats. More than once they were forced to give up in despair and come back later to try again.

We were introduced to the power of medications. During Catherine's fourth week of bed rest, she started having more contractions. The doctor placed her on *magnesium sulfate*, the strongest of all the drugs she received. This is a powerful muscle relaxant that stops uterine contractions; but the drug also has strong side effects, which can include respiratory arrest which leads to cardiac arrest.

Catherine's care throughout this month was absolutely the greatest. The best advice I can give anyone going into an extended hospital stay is to make friends with the nurses, the primary caregivers. They dispense medications, answer questions, give baths, and take vital signs. Catherine developed close friend-ships with her compassionate and professional nurses.

In Catherine's 26th week of pregnancy, her water broke; a tear developed in Henry's *amniotic sac*. The doctors were concerned that he would lose oxygen be-cause his umbilical cord could be squeezed by the uter-ine wall. His risk of infection increased. Numerous checks by the doctors also determined that Henry had dropped lower into Catherine's cervix. We joked that Henry was trying to kick his way out. We talked and pleaded with Henry, telling him to hang on, that it was not yet time for him to be born. I don't know if per-sonalities are formed in the womb, but this was Henry's way of telling us that he was going to be stubborn.

Catherine, her nurses and doctors did all they could to keep Henry and James from being born early. Through her own strength, and with the assistance of her medical care, Catherine was able to hang onto these babies for one very important month. Delivery at 22 weeks would have meant the almost certain death of our sons; delivered at 26 weeks they would have a chance. We later learned that the average length of time a woman actually makes it on bed rest prior to delivery is just four days. Catherine had beat the odds; her four weeks of bedrest had increased our sons' chances tremendously.

But there was another powerful element at work. It was during this long month we witnessed firsthand the ultimate and mighty power of prayer. So many

29

friends and family, and even people we didn't know, called or wrote to say that they were praying for Catherine and the boys. I firmly believe Catherine's strong faith in Jesus Christ and the prayers of many pulled her through.

As she hung onto these two unborn babies, she turned to the Lord for guidance. He did not disappoint her. He was there holding her hand, giving her strength and shining his incredible loving light onto our family. During that month Catherine's favorite Bible verse was Romans 15:13. "May the God of hope fill you with all joy and peace as you trust in Him, so that you may overflow with hope by the power of the Holy Spirit."

CHAPTER 4

Code Red

November 24, 1995

The birth of your children is supposed to be the greatest moment in your life as a parent. This was the case for my wife and me, but we would not realize it at that instant—or for many months to come. My memories of that day are not of the joy and excitment of seeing my children come into the world, or of hearing them cry for the first time, or of cutting the umbilical cord. My memories are of fear, confusion, and tears.

The previous night had been a nightmare for Catherine. We had eaten Thanksgiving dinner together in her room. She was fine as I left to go home and sleep. But later that night she started having contractions; she could not sleep, and she was pumped full of drugs. Fearful of losing these babies, she cried almost the entire night.

Early the next morning Dr.Williams came in to see how Catherine was doing. What he discovered was alarming. Her contractions had intensified—about one every 10 minutes. She had dilated to five centimeters and one of her cerclage stitches had torn. He found one of Henry's feet and his buttocks starting to come out. That was it! Dr. Williams informed Catherine that the babies needed to be delivered immediately! Catherine remembers hearing over the hospital's loudspeaker an order for *Code Red*. Only later did we find out that this Code Red order was for her and the babies.

I received the call at the ice rink. Although our due date was late February, our boys were ready to enter the world now, 14 weeks early. I drove frantically from the rink to Fairview-University Medical Center. When I arrived I was met by a nurse who told me that Catherine was not in her room but was already in the operating room being prepped for the emergency C-section. The nursing staff called both Catherine's and my parents.

A nurse told me to wash up, put on hospital scrubs, and wait for her to come get me. After changing, I waited for what seemed like ten minutes for the nurse to return. I felt, for the first time, some stress and anxiety. Finally, a different nurse came running and said frantically, "There you are; we've been waiting for you!" Things had gotten hectic in the operating room and they had temporarily forgotten me. There was no time for me to explain that I had been told to wait; she hurried me into the operating room where the surgical team was preparing for the emergency C-section.

The second I walked in, I knew the seriousness of the situation. I don't know whether I had been fooling myself or if I was just that naive, but I expected to enter the operating room and see a staff of four: Dr. Williams, an anesthesiologist and perhaps two nurses. What I found when I rushed though the door was an entire team of medical professionals: nurses, doctors, and respiratory therapists. In the midst of all this chaos, I saw Catherine on the operating bed. With my arrival, it made 13 of us packed into the operating room. A nurse guided me to a stool next to Catherine's head.

I now noticed all the high-tech medical equipment. I was completely awestruck, intimidated by the whole situation. I looked down at Catherine; she was experiencing a range of emotions. One second she was smiling, the next she was crying. I felt helpless. I tried to be of some comfort, holding her hand, rubbing her head, telling her everything would be just fine, although I now doubted that myself.

For the next hour, time stood still. I witnessed a truly spectacular event—doctors performing an emergency C-section on my wife. I have difficulty relating this life-changing experience even though now, five years later, I remember it like it was yesterday.

Catherine was given a spinal anesthesia. This allowed her to remain awake during the C-section, but she felt nothing below the chest. The doctor made a large incision into Catherine's abdomen. Using laser technology, he then cauterized the blood vessels to prevent excessive bleeding. This procedure created a terrible odor which I can best describe as the smell of hair burning.

Sitting on my stool, I did not have a good view of the procedure; a surgical sheet, like a small canopy, hung across the top of Catherine's chest so that she could not see the work the doctors were doing. To view everything, I had to stand up; I must have stood up and sat down 20 times during that operation. I would stand, watch part of the procedure—cutting her, pulling back the skin, clamping the tissue— sit back down and ask her in an exasperated voice, "Can't you feel that?" The whole experience was unreal.

Once the doctors had made the abdominal incision, they had to pull back the skin and connecting *adipose tissue* to expose the uterus. When a woman becomes pregnant, her abdominal wall becomes extremely thick; Catherine's must have been five to six inches thick. A cross section of this wall reminded me of macaroni. I was truly amazed by all of this, even as I continued to jump up to watch and then sit back down to comfort Catherine. I have always been fascinated with anatomy; and here I was, getting to see at close range inside a human body. What an education it was!

Next Dr. Williams made a cross-like incision in Catherine's uterus through which he would deliver the babies. This style of incision, I later learned, is common practice when a woman has a premature C-section. This early in the pregnancy, a woman's uterus has yet to stretch and become pliable.

I watched in wonder as Dr. Williams reached deep inside my wife; his hands seemed to disappear. When he removed them, they cradled a miniature, fragile being— Baby A, Henry. His defenseless body lay in the palm of Dr. Williams' hand. The doctor's other hand supported Henry's head.

Now I found out why there were so many people in the room. Dr. Williams immediately handed Henry to a nurse and cut the umbilical cord. The nurse turned and gently set him onto his surgical bed. Then Dr. Frank Mattea—a neonatologist—and two other nurses immediately began working on Henry. Only a moment later Dr. Williams lifted out Baby B, James; and the process was repeated with a different team of nurses and doctor. It was an amazing choreography of scrub-suited staff, babies, and equipment.

For me, it was a very terrifying moment: all these nurses and doctors working, struggling to pump life into these 26-week preemies. Infants this young and small are very fragile. No one knew at this moment whether these boys were going to live or die. Officially, the boys were born at 9:12 and 9:13 in the morning.

As father and husband, it was an excruciating time. I could not see my newly born sons; I would be in the way. I sat next to Catherine, who still remained on the operating table with her open incision. I tried to comfort her while her doctor and surgical nurse continued to check her for any problems.

Then two nurses and a doctor wheeled James toward us so that we could see him through the glass of his *Isolette.* Catherine cried immediately upon seeing her baby. I remember thinking to myself that this was perhaps the only time we would get to see him alive. We stared at him for about 30 seconds, and then the staff said they had to whisk him off to the intensive care unit. We did not get to see Henry at this time. He was too critical, and the staff was still working intensely on him in the corner of the operating room.

Now Catherine started experiencing sensation, so Dr. Williams instructed the anesthesiologist to put her out completely. I watched as the doctor pulled Catherine's uterus out through the gaping hole in her abdomen, set it on her stomach, and stitched up the incision in the uterus. I was totally in awe! I was told this procedure is relatively common in premature births and C-sections. Finally Dr. Williams inserted the uterus back into the opening and closed Catherine up. From surgery, my wife was wheeled to recovery, where she spent the next couple hours, slowly coming out of her anesthesia and surgery.

Catherine still remembers her fears going into surgery; she was overly tired, due to lack of sleep and from being on strong drugs. She can also recall viewing James momentarily in the operating room. She vaguely remembers being wheeled, while still groggy, into the Neonatal Intensive Care Unit (NICU) for a quick look at both boys before being returned to her own room.

About an hour after Catherine's C-section, a nurse escorted me into the NICU to see my sons. As I walked through the rooms, I saw for the first time just how tiny these neonates can be. I was frightened. The nurse led me to the back of the largest room. She pointed to an incubator about 15 feet away and said, "That is one of your sons." It was James. Two nurses were busily working on him, hooking up hoses and adjusting wires that were attached to his small body. I remember thinking that the nurses seemed pretty relaxed while they attended to James.

Then the nurse brought my attention to an area at our left and told me, "Your other son is over there." It was Henry. What I witnessed now was in sharp contrast to what I saw at James' station. Two doctors and two nurses were working on Henry, and it was anything but calm. The doctors bent over his tiny body, conferring with the nurses in medical lingo, spewing out names and numbers of medicines and dosage amounts; I did not understand any of it.

Henry was laid out on an open warmer bed that reminded me of a rolling cart that I use at school. The top shelf, the bed, was surrounded by a clear, short railing to prevent the baby from rolling off. Henry and his entire bed were vibrating very quickly. The sound and motion reminded me of a paint can shaker. I found out later that his little body was vibrating because a special kind of mechanical respirator called a *high frequency oscillator* was pumping oxygen down his throat and into his body in very fast puffs. Several wires were attached to Henry's arms, legs, and chest. I couldn't see his face; it was covered with tape holding his ventilator tube in position.

Placed on top of Henry was a piece of bubble wrap, the kind you could use to package fragile picture frames. This plastic wrap is used as heat or space blankets to keep premature babies warm. The doctors and nurses worked with a sense of urgency; all the while Henry's bed was vibrating. I could tell by their actions that things were serious.

My sons lay fighting for their lives and I couldn't touch them. I couldn't get any closer than ten feet from them. I thought I wanted a closer look, and yet a part of me just wanted to run out of that room as fast as I could. I was scared and confused. My nurse told me that we should probably leave and let the doctors and nurses do their work. I could come back in an hour or so when things hopefully would be settled down and more information was available.

By noon Dr. Sixto Guiang (Dr. X) and Dr. Frank came into our room to inform us of the severity and grave danger both Henry and James were in. The neonatologists doubted that our boys had reached 26 weeks' gestation; they were very tiny and immature even for that age. James measured just 34 centimeters (13.4 in.) and weighed 690 grams (1 lb., 8 oz.). Henry was even smaller: 32 centimeters (12.6 in.) and 670 grams (1 lb.,7.5 oz.) As hard as she tried, Catherine could not stay focused or alert. She knew her sons had been born, and that they were critically ill. She wanted information, but she kept falling asleep. It was like a bad dream from which she could not fully awaken.

Both sets of our parents were there with us, hoping and praying. I was a little confused about who I was supposed to be spending my time with. Should I be in the NICU, watching my sons as the hospital staff continued to work on them? Should I be caring for my wife as she tried to recover from surgery? Should I be visiting with our parents? The doctors and nurses were very helpful; they told me there was nothing I could do for my sons right then, and that until they had all the ventilators and IVs in and working, I could not be near my boys. It was best, they told me, to try and comfort my wife.

Throughout the afternoon, the NICU doctors kept us informed of Henry's and James' conditions. Not only were the boys extremely sick, but Dr. X told us there was a strong possibility that Henry was not going to make it. While James' condition was stabilizing and he was doing OK on the ventilator, Henry continued to struggle. He was too frail and was not responding to the ventilator. The staff suggested we make our arrangements with a pastor or priest—and to do it quickly. This conversation still rings clearly in my mind, five years later. The doctors, our parents, and the hospital chaplain left our room to give Catherine and me some time alone.

For me, this day was an emotional awakening. Seeing my sons born early and dealing with the uncertainty of their future caught me totally unprepared. Their birth awoke in me a new emotion. I love my wife dearly, but this love and caring for my sons was different. These children are a part of both Catherine and me. They were made by us, for us to care for. Every parent understands this feeling.

At the time of Henry's and James' birth, Catherine and I had been married six years; we had dated for five years before that. In those 11 years, Catherine had never once seen me cry. On the day the boys were born, Catherine and I, alone in her room, cried in each other's arms.

CHAPTER 5

Grace

January, 1995

Less than a year before the boys were delivered, Catherine had a pregnancy that ended in a miscarriage. Like many couples, with our first pregnancy we were excited; we told everyone right away, "We're pregnant!" Everything was new; excitement ran high. Then, when Catherine miscarried at 12 weeks, it was devastating—much more so for her than for me. It was a physical as well as an emotional nightmare for her. But the two of us had very different reactions and feelings (or lack of, in my case) concerning her miscarriage. She was devastated; she had lost a child she was carrying, one for whom she had developed a physical and loving bond.

I, on the other hand, had never felt this bond. Yes, I was excited about our impending parenthood. But when Catherine miscarried, I was much more worried about her and how she was coping than I was about the loss of our future child. I could tell she was in pain and that she felt this great loss. She tried to explain it to me many times without much success. Her tearful explanations failed to get through to me.

Not having carried this baby, and because the miscarriage was early in the pregnancy, I hadn't developed the strong parental yearnings that she had. Part of my thinking and feelings came from knowing several of our friends who had also miscarried. To me, this was just another part of trying to have a baby. It was no big deal; miscarriages happen all the time. If you lose the child, you just try again.

One thing I learned through our loss is that for most mothers, the life of a child begins immediately upon conception. For many men, including myself, it begins with the actual birth of that child. Morally, the women are more correct; there is life in the womb. That baby feeds off the mother, it grows inside her, it gains its strength from her. The child's features— fingers, toes, ears, nose, hair—develop while the fetus is in the womb. These miraculous developments create the strong mother-infant bond.

For the father, between conception and the birth there doesn't seem to be much for us to do. We can love our wife, comfort her, take birthing classes. Yes, we can talk to the baby, but we do not have that physical attachment yet. We can't hold the baby, we can't feed it, and we can't cuddle it. I felt more like a cheerleader, there to offer support and encouragement.

When there is a miscarriage, the husband and wife seem to go through different grieving processes. A recent article in the *Star Tribune* told of a couple who had gone through events similiar to Catherine's and mine. The wife gave birth to premature babies after previous miscarriages. Staff writer Kay Miller pointed out: "Women and men grieve differently. The wife needed to talk, and go over and over it. The husband would and could not open up. To him the loss was done and over with—'Let's move on.' He understood what she lost, but he couldn't wallow in loss anymore" (Miller, 2001).

An example of how Catherine and I grieved differently after the miscarriage is illustrated by the fact that she had named this baby. I, on the other hand, had almost completely forgotten over the last five years that she had done so. I was reminded of it when we talked about friends of ours who had recently miscarried. What makes me sad, and really showed me how we dealt with this situation differently, was that I had to ask Catherine what name she had given this child. I did not even remember the name—Grace.

CHAPTER 6

Love Through the Glass

November 25 - December 31, 1995

After a restless sleep in Catherine's hospital room, we awoke the next morning to the news that both boys were still alive...although Henry's condition was guarded. The boys were our two little miracles. The dictionary defines *miracle* as: "an event...thought to be due to supernatural causes, especially to an act of God." James and Henry were ours, but for how long? Their struggle for life had just begun. It was Catherine's 29th birthday.

At first the Neonatal Intensive Care Unit (NICU) was totally overwhelming to both Catherine and me. It took us a while to adjust to all the machines used in keeping premature babies alive. My first impression entering the NICU was like walking into a gambling casino without all the smoke. Lights were going on, alarms were going off, people were busy hustling around. The Fairview-University NICU is comprised of three large open rooms with babies in their incubators placed at stations around the perimeter of each room. Several babies are in covered Isolettes; some are in open warmers, and some are even in small bassinets or cribs, depending on their needs. Not all intensive care babies are tiny preemies; some are full-term babies with medical complications. Many infants have several pieces of medical equipment in and around their station: ventilators, heart rate monitors, IV stands and tubes, *apnea monitors*, and *oxygen saturation monitors*. These devices have alarms and lights that go off periodically. Listening to the warning buzzers for a dozen different babies can easily make one go into sensory overload.

Home, to Henry and James, were their baby Isolettes, in which heat and oxygen levels were carefully regulated. Through the glass windows of these incubators, we studied the boys' every feature. For the first week, we could not even hold our sons. We had to scrub up, put on latex gloves, and reach in through sleeves that were attached to two portholes in the side of their incubators. This allowed us to touch the boys without the threat of germs; but we were sad that the only physical contact with our newborn sons was through a pair of gloves.

As impersonal as the Isolette can look, Catherine and her mother took care to make sure the boys' quarters were as homey as possible. Each boy had an angel hung up in his Isolette to look over him— gifts from friends who had delivered a 23-week preemie four years earlier. Their son is thriving today. Stuffed turtles, perched atop their units, signified that though the boys may be slow starters, it is the steady progress that is important. Catherine taped to the sides of the Isolettes pictures of our family. The boys were wrapped in blankets or, at times, dressed in doll-size clothes that had been sewn by volunteers. Anything that went inside their quarters, including clothing, first had to be sterilized.

Due to the high risk for infection and the tiny size of most premature babies in intensive care, staff and parents had to practice sterile procedures. When we entered the NICU, we had to scrub up—lather, scrub, and rinse for three minutes. We repeated the whole process when we moved from one son to the other. Needless to say, Catherine and I both developed very chapped hands.

The health of the babies' visitors was also important. Babies this small and weak have less ability to fight off infections or germs. If we, the parents, or the grandparents were battling colds or had any respiratory infections, we were told not to come in. We wore surgical masks if we had minor cases of sniffles.

The hospital set restrictions on the number of visitors to the NICU. Not just anyone is allowed in. When the boys were born at 1½ pounds, both sets of our parents and two other persons whom we got to choose were placed on Henry and James' visitor list. For these spots we chose Catherine's sister Jane and my sister Kathleen. Later, we were able to sneak my brother Steve and Catherine's brother John in to see their tiny nephews on one or two occasions.

While Catherine was recovering from her C-section, she continued to have her own room just a short walk down the hall from the boys. She was able to spend her days and evenings watching and praying over her new sons. But the time came for Catherine to be discharged from the hospital. Five weeks after last seeing our house, she came home . . . without her babies.

This marked the beginning of a five-month period during which Catherine spent her nights at home, but returned daily to the hospital to keep her endless vigil over our sons. When the boys were one week old, James' primary nurse told us we could hold him. Knowing the importance of the bond between baby and parent, the neonatal staff practices a technique called *kangaroo care*, in which the baby is placed on the parent's bare chest. Studies have shown that newborns who are held or "kangarooed" develop better physically and have fewer developmental problems. We were terrified as we prepared to hold our son. It took two nurses to get James out of his Isolette, move the wires and oxygen hoses, and then place this 13-inch infant on Catherine's

47

chest. Overwhelmed, she cried as she held one of her babies for the first time.

Henry's condition stabilized, and three days after embracing James, Catherine held Henry. Once again she was overcome with emotion while she snuggled her son. As the nurses placed Henry back into his Isolette, we prayed that we would have another opportunity to hold him. Within a week or two, kangarooing became a daily event to which Catherine and I looked forward with great anticipation.

The many problems associated with prematurity can be overwhelming for the parents. Babies born before 30 weeks are almost always very sick. Both Henry and James had *intraventricular hemorrhaging* of the brain. These bleeds are graded on a scale of 1 to 4, with 1 being minor—not usually causing any severe long-term effects. Bleeds of grades 3 and 4 are known to be associated with long-term cognitive and developmental problems and cerebral palsy. James had a grade 2 bleed; Henry had a grade 3, borderline 4, bleed.

Both boys had underdeveloped lungs. They were placed on ventilators to assist their breathing and to provide them with sufficient oxygen. One major ingredient not yet produced within premature babies is *surfactant*. This soapy film—a combination of fats and proteins—coats the tiny air sacs of the lungs, allowing them to remain expanded. The boys were administered this protein artificially down their breathing tubes until they started producing their own.

Due to underdevelopment of some of the vital organs—stomach, kidneys, liver—these early preemies receive all nutrition intravenously. Based on each infant's daily lab results, the hospital pharmacy produces a *hyperalimentation,* a mixture of vitamins, minerals, and proteins. In the NICU this IV nutrition is jokingly referred to as "Mountain Dew" because of its color and consistency.

Using IV lines for feedings and delivery of medications presents another problem, however. The doctors and nurses have great difficulty finding a vein or artery large enough to handle an IV in an infant this small. In addition, preemies' veins and arteries are very brittle and shred or break easily. An infant who needs several medications, or who needs IVs over a long period of time, may require a surgically-implanted central line. Both our sons had central lines implanted into their umbilical cords and their groins. Henry needed four separate IV lines at one time to accommodate the eight to ten different medications he required.

One day we would come to the hospital and see that the boys had an IV in a foot; the next day it would be in an arm. The worst shock was the time we came to the NICU and discovered Henry had two IVs in his head. Catherine and I both cried over that. Another time an IV infiltrated Henry's head, and he developed a huge black and blue bruise that covered the entire side of his head. Today both boys bear scars from those early infiltrations.

Henry's charts showed he had 17 different medical complications associated with his prematurity. With all these problems, at times the whole situation seemed desperate. Right from the day of their birth, James was our leader. He seemed to have a quiet confidence about him as he lay in his incubator. Within a few days, his weight had dropped to one pound, three ounces. This weight drop, due to loss of excess water, was expected and happens with nearly all newborns. Where James found the ounces to lose, we don't know; we could already count each protruding rib. Henry did not drop weight, a sign of future problems that worried the hospital staff.

While we cried almost daily in anguish over Henry and his constant battles for strength and health, James was our miracle son— growing, getting stronger, non-verbally telling us, "I'm okay, don't worry; Henry needs you." Due to his steadying effect on us all, we were caught off guard when in December, after weeks of calm, we arrived at the hospital to find James in distress. He had developed a blood infection and the doctors and nurses were worried about his ability to fight this disease. We were scared. We had thought for sure James was going to be OK; now we worried about possibly losing both sons. With antibiotics and skilled care, James fought his way back to health. This was another evidence of answered prayer.

In the NICU, we saw other premature babies, underdeveloped, sick, fighting for their lives. Some of these babies did not survive. For weeks we would see a baby and its parents, going through the same things that we were. Then one day we might come in and find out that the baby had died. This hit both Catherine and me hard; it would bring us to tears. We tried to imagine what the babies' parents were going through. One reason this was so stressful for us was that we knew how sick our own boys were. In the back of our minds we thought that we could be the next to lose our child.

One factor that added to my fears was that I could not be at the hospital through every crisis. I had traveled to Duluth to coach my hockey team in a three-game tournament. Early in the second morning of my absence, Catherine called me from the hospital. She was in tears; Henry had worsened overnight. His kidneys were failing and he was not passing fluids. The doctors told Catherine his condition was critical and that I should come to the hospital as soon as possible. I could hear the fear in her voice as she cried, "Jon, I don't know what to do; Henry might not make it!"

I drove the 2½ hours to the hospital. By the time I got there, Henry had urinated and was doing better. He was temporarily out of danger. Catherine and I spent all of that day and evening in the NICU. After a short night's sleep, I drove back to Duluth for our final game.

When a parent has a child on an extended hospital stay, his career or work becomes secondary. Though many days I did not feel like I should be at work, we still had a mortgage to pay; we needed money for groceries. In my elementary-school gym classes, a student's struggle to bounce a ball or run a half mile seemed insignificent to me while I wondered if my sons would survive the day.

I remember the mixed emotions I felt as I would lace up my skates and step out onto the ice to coach my high school team in a practice. Stretching my legs, breaking a sweat, and feeling the cold crisp air surging through my lungs was a much-needed temporary catharsis for me. But it also was hard for me to watch these skilled 17 and 18-year-old athletes as they practically danced across the ice, forward and backward on the thin edge of their skate blades. I was preoccupied with wondering if my sons would ever learn to walk. I, like other parents in similiar circumstances, learned to cope the best I could.

Eventually the stress level became unbearable. During the first weeks after the boys' birth, everyone at my school was so concerned about how Henry and James were doing. Every time I ran into a colleague, he or she would ask, "How are the twins? Are they OK?" It got to the point that I felt I was answering these questions

30 times a day. I knew they cared and they had our family's best interest at heart. But it was too painful for me to rehash everything repeatedly.

Finally at a staff meeting I broke down. I stood up and thanked everyone for their concern, but I was losing my mind, repeating the details of our latest crises time and time again. I asked them if they could just relax their concern a little bit, and in my own due time I would inform them of Henry's and James' conditions. This was a selfish act on my part, but I could not go on answering everyone's requests; I felt outmatched, 30 against one. Luckily, I got to leave that meeting right after finishing my announcement. As I walked out, tears were rolling down my cheeks. I never have thanked my coworkers properly for all their concern and for allowing me a little bit of space. I owe a special debt of gratitude to my former teaching partner Sara, who supported me during this difficult time.

The last week of December brought us the holiday season, a season of giving. This was true in the hospital as well. All the babies received Santa Bears during a visit from St. Nick. After spending most of the day rocking and singing to the boys at the NICU, Catherine and I attended the annual Westby Christmas Eve gathering at my Uncle Jim's house. It was nice to be with family: between 50 and 60 aunts, uncles, cousins, grandchildren, and our patriarch— Henry Olaf Westby, my grandfather and Henry's and James' great-grandfather. My father read a stirring poem he had written for Henry and James. I noticed several family members wipe tears from their eyes as they listened.

On Christmas Day, we traveled to Catherine's parents' house, which they had decorated in the usual beautiful Christmas spirit. The food was, as always, exceptional in taste and in presentation. Though we cherished these times with caring family, both Catherine and I found our thoughts remained back in the NICU.

Wearing party hats, Catherine and I celebrated New Year's Eve quietly in the hospital. We would have preferred being at home with Henry and James, but a quiet New Year's Eve rocking our boys to sleep was the best New Year's present we could have asked for.

While Catherine and I were dealing with the pressures of having twin sons in the NICU, our boys continued their struggle for life. Every day either a new hurdle was passed or a new problem arose. One day they would be doing fine and the next day they would take a turn for the worse. The boys fought hard. They were proving to be strong-willed, but would it be enough?

CHAPTER 7

Henry's Last Chance

January 13, 1996

Henry was an extremely sick micro-preemie. Among all the other problems relating to his prematurity, he had a heart defect. This defect was not diagnosed until he was a week old, when doctors discovered that the blood pressure in Henry's lower extremities was lower than the blood pressure in his upper extremities. The readings in his arms were normal, but the readings taken in his legs showed that he was not receiving a proper blood flow. An echocardiographer discovered the abnormality after examining Henry and completing an ultrasound of his heart. These tests revealed a narrowing in his aorta, which was shaped like an hour glass. The condition was called a *coarctation of the aorta*. Blood would back up above the narrowing instead of flowing smoothly through.

This problem became life-threatening for Henry because his vital organs located in his lower half—his liver, kidney, and intestines—were not receiving enough blood flow for them to work correctly. Surgeons can correct this abnormality by performing a procedure called a *sub-clavian flap repair*. The surgeon enlarges the narrowing in the aorta by making an incision and splicing part of another artery together with the aorta. The doctors described it to us as a flap which is made of the patient's own tissue and grows together with the aorta, making a larger vessel. In some instances surgeons use synthetic materials to enlarge the aorta.

Due to Henry's size and frailty, the cardiologist and the surgeon said it would be impossible to perform this operation on him. The size and brittleness of his arteries would make the operation way too risky. The NICU doctors and the surgeon agreed that they would do the required surgery when Henry grew to four pounds.

But instead of growing larger and stronger, Henry grew weaker and his condition deteriorated. We realized he wouldn't get to four pounds. With all we had already gone through, this was the most discouraging of all— watching Henry get sicker and sicker. Part of our first month in the NICU had taught us to expect the unexpected and not to be surprised. But it was heartbreaking to watch our own baby fail, not knowing if we would ever get to take him home.

Henry sometimes gained a half pound overnight because he was not urinating due to kidney and liver failures caused by the coarctation. His entire abdomen became a large black and blue water balloon. Then, by some miracle, he would pee and the swelling would go down. Pictures we have of him from this period reveal just how ill he really was. I still develop a lump in my throat whenever I look at them.

Week by week, Henry continued to get worse. Most of the staff was amazed that he had lived through all of his complications. What Henry was showing us was his incredible fighting spirit and his will to live. Every week a new crisis would arise; and just when things looked their bleakest, Henry would rise up again and surprise us.

The NICU doctors were forced to make a decision. With our permission, they would try to convince the surgeon that this operation was Henry's only hope of survival. Without it, Henry's kidneys and liver would fail completely. They also told us that because of Henry's size and lack of strength, there was a strong chance that he would die on the operating table—especially if the surgeon could not enlarge his aorta.

With persuasion and arm twisting from the NICU doctors, Dr. John Foker, a pediatric cardiac surgeon, agreed to the surgery. Catherine and I gave our permission without hesitation. We had spent so much time with Henry that first month. We knew how sick he was; we had seen how much he had struggled in his short life already. As for me, I prayed for a successful surgery; but I also knew that if the surgery did not work, I would let him go. Henry had already suffered too much. Catherine remembers telling God to "take Henry or heal him." She could not bear his suffering any more.

The day of the surgery was endless. Henry was transported by ambulance early that morning from the NICU, which was located at the Fairview-Riverside Campus, across the river to the Fairview-University Campus. Catherine rode along with Henry in the ambulance. Our parents and sisters and I all met Henry and Catherine in the pre-surgery suite where we spent a couple hours prior to the operation. This contingent of loving family milled around a tiny, sick baby, hoping and praying, waiting for him to go off to surgery.

It was an incredibly emotional wait. I watched as each person took his turn crying, caressing Henry, wishing him the best of luck. At one point I sat in the corner of the room, a solitary figure, watching Catherine and all our family gathered around Henry, all fighting to keep their composure. As I witnessed this, I began to weep. I cried like I had not cried in years. I thought to myself that our families were saying goodbye to Henry. The previous weeks seemed to all come crashing together at this one point and I could not stop the tears.

For a few moments our families left Catherine and me alone with Henry. I rested my chin on Henry's bed, my face just inches from him. I rubbed his bruised abdomen and told him how much I loved him. Then, it was time to go. In a procession, we all walked Henry to the elevators. The nurses and doctors finally took him for his surgery. We were not sure if we would see him alive again.

While Henry was in surgery we busied ourselves with drinking coffee, reading the paper, and walking around. Whenever a door opened, we would jump to attention. After about two hours the surgeons sent word that they had successfully opened Henry up, and he was doing fine so far.

Finally, after four hours, Dr. Catherine Bendel, one of Henry's neonatologists, came out to the waiting room. She began telling us how amazed she was that Henry's aorta was indeed shaped exactly as the cardiologist had predicted. It looked like an hour glass. She mentioned how fascinating it was to watch as blood would flow, then stop, then flow some more, passing through the narrowing in Henry's aorta. Finally, my father-in-law interupted, "Doctor, is Henry all right? Is he still alive?"

"Oh, I'm so sorry," she answered. "Yes, the surgery is a remarkable success! They're just finishing closing him up; he'll be in recovery within the hour." Dr. Foker soon joined us and described how he had had to improvise. He had taken the large sub-clavian artery from Henry's left shoulder and patched it together with his aorta to create a larger vessel through which the blood could freely flow. As the surgeon spoke, our families were amazed to think how this 6'4" surgeon with enormous hands had successfully operated on this tiny baby.

All of us, including the surgeon, were elated. Henry had made it! Our anxiety and sorrow gave way to euphoria. Tears flowed from family members, but these were tears of joy. Even Dr. Bendel and the surgeon were surprised at how well Henry's tiny veins and arteries held up. Dr. Foker said Henry's aorta was the size of a spaghetti noodle. Due to this surgery and because his sub-clavian artery is adjoined to his aorta, Henry's blood pressure cannot be taken in his left arm.

After recovery, Henry was transported back across the river to the NICU to join his brother. What a truly remarkable day it turned out to be. As family and friends prayed, a dying baby survived a risky surgery. It was a miracle come true. It was not only the skill of Henry's talented surgeons that saved his life; it was also an answer to hundreds of prayers.

In February of 1996, the *Star Tribune* featured an article about the boys, concentrating on Henry's successful heart surgery at a record small size—less than two pounds (Slovut, 1996). For several years, a framed copy of this article has been posted on the wall just outside the neonatal unit at Fairview-

Riverside Medical Center. This published story and Henry's scar, which circles under his left arm, are two reminders of our small son's unwavering will to live.

CHAPTER 8

Godmothers from the NICU

Winter 1996

Little did I know the day the boys were born, that for the next 5½ months Henry, James, Catherine, and I would call the NICU *home*. Initially, it was hard not to become anxious every time an alarm sounded or light flashed, but the nurses taught us the importance of looking at the big picture. Alarms that sound, babies that cry, or doctors scurrying around most often are good things. As the boys' stay in the NICU grew longer, Catherine and I became more familiar and comfortable with our surroundings.

One week after Henry's heart surgery, we had another cause for celebration: James came off of the ventilator. That day we heard, for first time, one of our sons cry. While the boys were intubated we could see them showing distress yet making no sound. Catherine described their predicament as "insult added to injury";

crying and yet being unable to vocalize it. James' first real cry was so soft we had to put our ears down close to actually hear anything. A baby's cry is a common occurrence, but our son's cry caused our family to weep with joy.

Henry remained on a ventilator for 3½ months because of underdeveloped lungs and also because of his heart surgery. Although the ventilator was essential to his breathing, the additional oxygen has negative side effects. Excess oxygen can cause vision problems and potential blindness. Very early preemies are also vulnerable for future vision problems because the retina is usually not fully developed until the 44th week post-conception.

During Henry's prolonged stay in the NICU, we were asked if we would be willing to place him in a study called STOP R.O.P. (Retinopathy of Prematurity) being conducted through the University of Minnesota. Ophthalmology researchers were looking to see if oxygen saturation levels at or above 98% helped improve babies' eyesight. Premature babies on ventilators are generally administered oxygen at levels between 88% and 95%.

Using a staging scale of 1 to 5, with 5 being permanent *retinal detachment*, tests showed Henry had a pre-threshold R.O.P. of Stage 2 in one eye and Stage 3 in the other. Stage 3 is the threshhold for surgery. After discussing the possible risks or benefits to our child, Catherine and I agreed to the study.

The test was administered in a double blind format. One group of babies would receive the extra oxygen and another group would remain on their current amount. The doctors in charge of the study did not know which babies were receiving the extra oxygen until after the results of the study were compiled. As parents, we also would never know into which group our son fell. What I do know is that by another small miracle Henry has no current vision problems.

After three months in the hospital, Henry grew weary of the ventilator tube down his throat, so he started taking matters into his own hands. His solution to this annoying tube was to lick off the tape around the sides of his mouth—tape which held the tube in place. He would then try to pull the tube out. Henry was again showing us his strong will and stubbornness that I have grown to admire and love. However, his lungs were not yet strong enough to pump the necessary oxygen. Whenever he dislodged the ventilator tube, his oxygen monitor would go off; he would stop breathing, and the nurse would have to manually pump oxygen into him until the doctors could *reintubate* him. Henry did this three or four times over a two-week period.

Our neonatal nurse practitioner (NNP) decided the staff could not risk Henry's *extubating* himself again. Previous attempts to wean him off the ventilator had been unsuccessful; he would breathe on his own for a couple hours then begin to struggle, necessitating a reintubation. Doctors advised us they would perform a *tracheostomy* through which they would give Henry assisted oxygen. The tube down his throat would then be removed. That day Catherine cried and pleaded with the NNP to allow Henry just one more day to see if he could somehow grow strong enough to handle the breathing on his own. The practitioner, an incredibly caring and loving soul, gave in. "Tomorrow is it!" she said. "We extubate him, and if he can't sustain his oxygen levels, he will receive a tracheostomy."

The next day came; it was the morning after we had taken James home from the hospital. Once again—to no one's surprise—Henry had started the extubation process himself. He had again licked off the tape from around his mouth and was trying to pull his breathing tube out. As Catherine looked on in anticipation, the nurses and doctors finished the job Henry had started. They took the breathing tube out of his throat, and wouldn't you know it—that determined little guy started breathing on his own! A whiff of oxygen was added into his nose through a *C-PAP* (continuous positive airway pressure) device for support. Another miracle and another reason to cry tears of joy.

The next benchmark took place when the boys matured and grew enough to start being fed breast milk, which Catherine had been pumping and storing. Until this time both boys received all their nourishment intravenously. James' first milk feeding was at five weeks. Henry had to wait until he had recovered from his heart surgery. These first feedings were

65

administered by *gavage*, putting a narrow tube in through the nose and down the throat into the stomach and dripping the milk in. One cc (½ tsp) was the amount they were given for their first few feedings. I was amazed at how meager these feedings were. As long as the boys remained on the ventilators, the gavage feedings continued but were supplemented with the intravenous nutrients.

Catherine had tried, unsuccessfully, to get James to nurse shortly after he was extubated. But he was not yet strong enough to suck, so the gavage feedings were continued. Two or three weeks later, when he had grown a little stronger, Catherine made another attempt to teach James to breastfeed. But it again proved futile for many reasons. Extended use of the ventilator can lead to throat and mouth problems in preemies. This is exactly what happened with our boys; their ability to suck and breastfeed was greatly impaired because the ventilator tube had created grooves in the roofs of their mouths. They had also developed a degree of oral aversion from having the breathing tubes in their mouths for so long.

In addition, while Catherine was trying to nurse James, she also pumped breast milk to store for Henry; he was not yet ready for milk feedings. The stress of this, in addition to dealing with life in the NICU, all made nursing difficult. The lactation specialist and the doctor put James on a special preemie formula; Catherine kept pumping for Henry for several more weeks. Catherine and the nurses experimented with several styles of nipples before finding the one the boys responded to best. The nursing bottles were the size of toy bottles.

As the boys' condition stabilized, Catherine's days became more normal in routine. It is just that these days were spent in the hospital and not in the privacy of our own home. Her hours in the NICU were filled with feeding, bathing, rocking and singing to the boys. She could do this and visit with her new friends, the boys' primary nurses. As time went on, Catherine became familiar with the boys' equipment and alarms; she would just turn them off herself or move something if she thought it didn't belong there. She was able to take over much of the routine nursing duties for the boys. Catherine kept meticulous notes of medical terminology and definitions. She could confer intelligently with the staff, using important-sounding medical terms: *dobutamine, respiratory distress syndrome, hyperalimentation* and *coarctation* repair. We joked that she was earning an honorary degree in medicine.

About three weeks after Henry's heart surgery, Catherine received the news that we had not dared to hope for. She sat by his Isolette listening in as Dr. Georgieff led a group of interns through their daily rounds. As they finished discussing Henry's complicated case history, Dr. Georgieff turned to my wife and said, "You know, Catherine, the roller coaster ride is almost over. There is a 95 percent probability that you will take *two* boys home one day." This was the first time Catherine had been assured that Henry was going to make it.

Due to hospital privacy policies, we did not know much about the neighboring babies. There is a "hands off policy;" the nurses can't tell you about other babies, so you're not supposed to ask. As parents, we wanted to give the other parents and their baby the privacy that we coveted so dearly. But Catherine developed a friendship with one mother whose baby girl was in the station between Henry's and James'. For many weeks we would see this very sick baby and her parents. It was obvious they were a loving couple.

This baby did eventually die, and Catherine took it particularly hard. She asked one of the boys' primary nurses if it was permissible to send a letter of condolence to the parents. The nurse said that was fine and that she would forward the letter to the couple. Catherine wrote them a message of compassion. She told them we had become attached to their baby in the NICU and that we were sad for them that their baby passed away. Catherine included our phone number and address and asked the mother to call if she felt up to it. The two women, both devout Christians, developed a strong bond and they remain friends to this day. We found out later that this baby to whom we had grown so attached had been a surviving twin; the other twin, a boy, had died in utero.

The greatest asset of this NICU is its staff. Yes, the unit was technologically first-rate, but that was secondary to the skill and compassion shown by these dedicated professionals. The doctors, nurses, respiratory therapists were all top notch. We became good friends with Henry and James' primary nurses, their main caregivers. Catherine cried on their shoulders many times. These women grew to love Henry and James, and I observed the incredible passion they brought to their work. As our sons would pass certain milestones, their primaries were as ecstatic as we were. When the boys went into distress, we could see the pain and sorrow in our nurses' eyes.

Henry's primary nurse Kari exemplified the depth of love these nurses showed toward our boys. The day of Henry's heart surgery, she insisted on extending her work shift so that she could escort Henry in the ambulance to the Fairview-University East Campus. She wanted to see Henry one last time and to comfort Catherine and me. When she left for home and a few hours sleep, tears rolled down her cheeks. After hearing of the successful surgery, she came back early to see Henry again before starting her next shift in the NICU.

Sometimes Catherine and I would take short breaks from the hospital and walk across Riverside Avenue to Starbucks for a cup of coffee, or a latte in Catherine's case. Once we found out our nurses also loved lattes, we never came back empty handed. They would put up a fuss—something about hospital policy and gifts—but they always gave in. These nurses spoiled us, doing special favors for us on occasion. From the lounges they would heist large, comfortable sliding rocking chairs into the NICU for our kangarooing sessions. We were allowed to relax or eat in the nurses' lounge during quiet times. By the end of our time in the NICU, our primary nurses meant so much to us that we asked them to be Henry's and James' godmothers. They happily accepted.

I don't remember how many games my hockey team won that winter. I don't remember how many feet of snow I shoveled from our sidewalk and driveway. But at the hospital Catherine and I recorded each new sign of progress and watched as the boys slowly gained ounces and inches. We looked forward to spring, confident that we would bring James home by Easter. We could only hope that Henry would make it home for Mothers' Day.

We treasured the peaceful times in the NICU. In the late evenings the nurses turned down the alarms and lights and placed quilts over the Isolettes. The number of staff and visitors was minimal. Most nights after work, I met Catherine at the hospital and we would kangaroo and rock our boys for long stretches. These were cherished times that made us happy and hopeful.

CHAPTER 9

Coming Home

March--May, 1996

Our early days in the NICU seemed to last forever. But once our two little miracles began to thrive and develop, time in the NICU started to fly by more quickly. Before we knew it, it was March and James was ready to come home. As I look back at our stay in the NICU, it was a short chapter of our history.

Bringing James home from the hospital was both a joyous yet difficult experience. On March 8, after his first 3½ months of life—all spent in the hospital—James was ready to come home. He now weighed nearly five pounds, was eating well, and had been off of the ventilator for over a month. For this we rejoiced; it was an answer to our prayers. For all the joy and happiness we felt in being able to bring James home, we probably felt more sadness and sorrow in the fact that Henry was not ready to come home.

During these first months of life, the boys lived and slept just a few feet away from each other. Now James was going home, but his brother, his friend, was going to be left behind. Henry and James may have been too young to know or understand what was going on, but it would be the first time they were separated.

The hospital prepares the parents for taking their child home. Because they had experienced some minor *apnea* episodes while in the hospital, the boys were coming home on *apnea monitors.* Catherine and I, our parents, and our sisters were given courses in reading and responding to the monitor and in infant CPR. Henry would also be coming home on medications; we were educated in the finer points of meds, dosage and delivery. Getting ready to bring the boys home was exciting, but also a little nerve-racking. During these months we had the best care available at our finger tips; but now we would have to go it alone. Catherine and I commented to each other that there was so much to learn.

In the previous months I had often ridden the elevator with beaming new parents, excited to be taking their infant home after a one or two-day stay in the hospital. James' homecoming, after nearly four months in the hospital, was a real celebration. Catherine and I were not alone in this event; our parents were there, as well as our sisters. The nurses and other hospital staff joined in the festivities, shedding tears of happiness.

Our family shot rolls of film this day; the pictures show the elation on everyones' faces.

After the NICU staff finished their farewells, we took James to say goodbye to his brother Henry one last time. Then James' primary nurse Grace escorted James, Catherine, and me through the hospital's main door out into the cold and windy March day. As Grace said goodbye to him and then hugged Catherine, she cried. I believe these were tears of joy for the miracle of James' life. Catherine and I drove away with mixed emotions: excited to be bringing one baby home and yet sad that Henry must remain behind. There is a term used when parents go home without their child: "empty arms." Catherine cried the entire drive home because she felt we were abandoning Henry.

There was a two-month period when James was at home but Henry was still in the NICU. Because I was working all day, life for Catherine got really crazy and stressful. She needed to be up at the hospital with Henry, but initially James was not allowed up there. Catherine's greatest stress and fears were of leaving Henry each day; he was still considered an "at risk" preemie. She wanted to be there to care for him and to discuss his progress with the doctors. But James also needed to adjust to his new home. Although he was more than three months old, he was barely five pounds and needed the attention that any newborn does. How could she meet the needs of both sons?

Because she had to be absent from the hospital several hours each day, our families increased their visits to Henry. Catherine was thankful, yet somewhat hurt and even resentful. She was Henry's mother; it was she who was supposed to be there for him, changing him, feeding him, or rocking him to sleep. At this time, she was also trying to pump and produce breast milk for Henry. With all of these pressures, Catherine was exhausted.

Some days one of our parents would come over to watch James so Catherine could go up to the hospital. My parents live very near Fairview-Riverside, so sometimes Catherine brought James over to their house and then headed over to see Henry. I was done coaching hockey for the season, so I would go up to the hospital right after teaching. Many days Catherine would wait until I got there and then the three of us—Henry, Catherine and I—would hang out and have some quality time together. After Catherine would leave, I would stay with Henry into the evening hours.

The NICU had an isolation room right off of the main room. This room was used for babies that came in extremely sick or infected and could not be in with the other premature babies. Many times this room was not in use, so in Henry's last month of stay he was often moved in there. We appreciated this room because it allowed us to bring James up to visit his brother. Henry's stay in the NICU was much longer than most babies', so in his last month of hospital care he was already five months old. The isolation room allowed him peace and quiet. The staff thought we deserved more quality family time together. This private room also prepared Henry and us for his going home; it was a godsend for us. Being tucked away from the hustle and bustle and lights and alarms was very comforting. But whenever a sick baby was admitted, Henry was moved back into the regular room with all the other babies.

As Henry's discharge day grew closer, his primary nurses became a little concerned for Catherine. Nurses mentioned to my mother more than once that they did not know how Catherine was going to manage once she had both boys home alone during the day because Henry needed constant attention. He was a fussy baby and would often arch his back, flail his arms and legs, and scream. He was difficult to bottle feed. At the time there seemed to be no medical or neurological reasons for these behaviors. The staff was certain that they would be re-admitting Henry within a week. Concern or no concern, the time was soon at hand for Henry to say goodbye.

But his coming home day would be postponed at the last minute. In addition to all his other complications, Henry had developed an *inguinal hernia*. The surgeons originally had planned on his going home and then coming back in to have it repaired, but the neonatalogists decided it should be repaired before he left. This procedure and recovery postponed his trip home for one week.

Finally the day arrived! Henry was ready to come home and join our family. We brought James back for the big event. Members of our family were here this day also. Again we held a farewell party and took many pictures of the nurses and doctors. We were saying our final goodbyes to a place we had called home for nearly six months. Just as we were getting him dressed to go home, the lab decided that they needed one more sample of Henry's blood. The technicians quickly scrambled to draw the sample before we left. We laughed as we told them, "Come on, enough already! You've had him for a half year; it's time for us to go."

Henry's primary nurse Bobbi escorted us to the hospital's main entrance, carrying her little patient one last time. We bid our tearful final farewell. As we loaded both boys into the car, I remember thinking to myself, *What a great, caring, and nurturing hospital this place has been.*

As happy as we were to finally be bringing Henry home, we were very sad to be leaving all of the wonderful staff at the NICU. Over the previous months we had shared so much with these people: we had laughed with them, cried with them, leaned on them, and they became part of our extended families and we part of theirs. They had acted as surrogate mothers to Henry and James, feeding them, changing them, nursing them to life. They also had helped Catherine tremendously by sharing with her, teaching her, giving her a shoulder to cry on, and encouraging her. They went way beyond the call of duty.

The doctors were extraordinary—so knowledgeable and giving of their time. I was amazed at how loving and compassionate they were towards Henry and James. I can never thank the staff at the NICU enough. All I can tell them is, "Thank you, we miss you; and forgive us for not staying in touch as often as we should have."

CHAPTER 10

The Power of Prayer

Summer 2001

In my eyes Henry and James are miracles. The care they received from their doctors and nurses was phenomenal, but a higher power played an even greater role. Whenever I get a little down or start worrying about their development, I think back to their birth and the months in the NICU, and I see the miles that they have already covered in their young lives. Today they are happy, loving, caring boys full of spirit.

A few days after the boys' birth, Catherine asked Doctor Frank about the prognosis for the boys' development. The doctor, knowing all the medical crises that the boys were going through—underdeveloped lungs, grade 3 brain bleeds, and being attached to a ventilator—answered, "They will know that they are loved."

Catherine sobbed when she received this news. To think that Henry and James have gone from *they will know that they are loved* to getting ready to start kindergarten this fall is evidence of God's grace.

I cannot begin to count the many people who prayed for Catherine and the boys. Not only our family and extended family, but friends and colleagues, strangers, members of our church and our parents' churches. Relatives in California and Wisconsin called to say they were praying. It was truly an incredible outpouring of prayer. I remember noticing one day a church bulletin lying on a table at my parents' house. On the back cover was stated: "We continue to pray for Henry and James Westby, grandsons of Dick and Sandy."

In the New Testament book of James 5:15-16 we read, "The prayer of faith will save the sick, and the Lord will raise him up. Confess your trespasses to one another and pray for one another, that you may be healed. The effective, fervent prayer of a righteous man avails much." During the boys' first few months we evidenced continuous praying for their lives and well-being. These prayers were heard and answered.

Henry and James experienced the power of prayer almost immediately upon birth. On that day our families were with us at the hospital. After being informed by the NICU doctors that we should make arrangements for Henry's near certain death, our parents and a hospital chaplain left Catherine and me alone in our hospital room to comfort each other. Unbeknowst to us, this

79

group—all with their own individual spiritual strength—was allowed into the NICU to pray over Henry and James. My father-in-law and my mother have each described to me, on separate occasions, how powerful and passionate this prayer was: our parents, my sister, and a hospital chaplain—standing and holding hands, praying over the bodies of two tiny babies.

Our family saw God's grace in many different forms. One day at work I found $20 in my school mailbox with a note attatched to it: "Praying for you, hope all goes well, hope you and Catherine get a chance to go out and get some coffee or see a movie."

Catherine had quit her job, and my teaching salary suddenly had to support four. We were so busy tending to the needs of our sons that our bill-paying took a back seat. We found ourselves in debt. Soon after, a $500 check arrived anonymously from our church. Friends from a school at which I had previously taught also collected money for us. Gale, a friend from church, purchased parking permits for our two vehicles, allowing us to park free in the hospital parking ramp during the months our boys were hospitalized.

After James came home, but while Henry remained in the hospital, friends volunteered to watch James, enabling Catherine to visit her other son. Several families brought us meals. When one receives so much grace, it becomes easy to return the gesture. Hopefully, Catherine and I have done this.

My wife and I found encouragement from other areas. We joined a small group from our church; these people have become some of our dearest and closest friends. This group prays for each other, looks out for each other, and is always ready to give a helping hand.

Another source of support for Catherine came from joining a group called "Mothers of Multiples." This organization is exactly what the title reflects— moms who have given birth to twins, triplets, quads, etc. The group is highly organized and Catherine took to it right away. She developed close friendships and gained valuable knowledge and support from these women.

Both Catherine and I recognize our responsibility in helping Henry and James build a strong foundation for a future faith in Christ. We continued to pray *for* James and Henry daily. We now pray *with* our two sons every night before we tuck them into bed. Since the age of four, they have traded off doing the praying with us. Recently, it has been amusing because James has again been showing his loving and caring soul. On the nights he has his turn, we can expect a prayer lasting at least three minutes as he blesses everything from Mommy and Daddy to Buzz Lightyear and *Toy Story 2*. A couple nights a week we read to them from their beginner Bible book. The boys now readily recognize and identify Bible stories. Henry's favorite characters are Goliath and Samson, which is fitting since he's so small.

Catherine and I both want the boys to develop into young men of high character. But when asked about our boys, we give different types of responses. For example, at the boys' first birthday party, someone asked me, "What are your wishes for your sons' futures?"

I answered, "I hope they do well in school, make a lot of friends, maybe one day get married, get a good job, and I hope that they like sports."

Soon I heard this person ask Catherine the same question. She answered emphatically, " I hope they have a strong spirit and know that we love them." Two very different answers from two parents who equally love their children. Catherine's answer signifies to me just how important it is to her to pass along to our sons her passionate belief in Jesus Christ. She swears to this day that the strongest her faith has ever been was while the boys were in the hospital. She prayed daily and felt certain that her prayers were being heard and that good things were going to come from her prayers. She was right.

I am confident and hopeful that with Catherine's devotion, and all the prayers that the boys have received over the years, and all the incidents of grace being shown our family—that Henry and James will grow up with the same strong faith that their mother has.

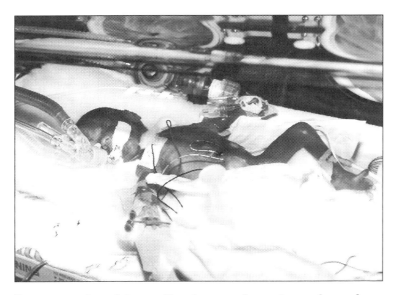

James receives his medications and nutrients through a central line. Tape across his face holds ventilator tube in place. (November 27, 1995)

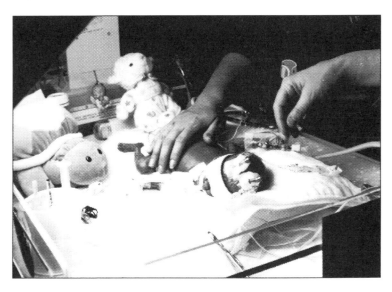

Henry's turtle looks on as Catherine and nurse Kari comfort Henry. Two IV lines in his head deliver medications. (December, 1995)

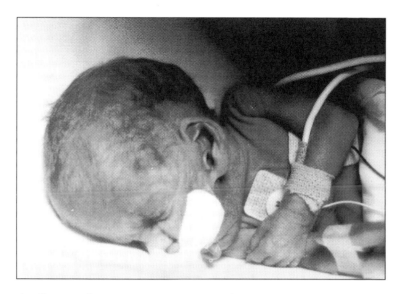

As James sleeps, monitors record his heart beat and oxygen saturation levels. (December, 1995)

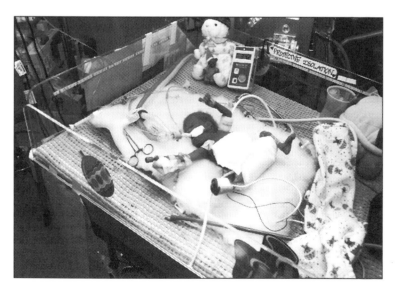

Henry lies in an open warmer bed, amidst medical equipment and stuffed animals. (January 1, 1996)

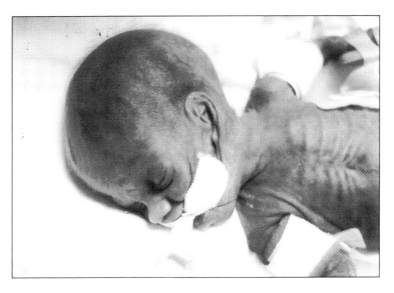

Henry's protruding ribs and his bruised head, where IV
lines had infiltrated, were just two indications of his
frailty. (January 10, 1996)

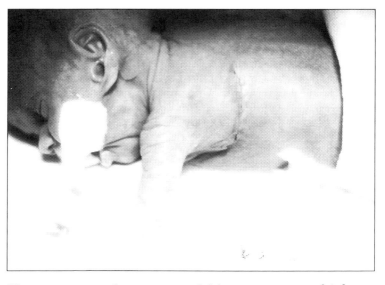

Henry recovers from successful heart surgery, which
repaired his spaghetti-thin aorta. (January 20, 1996)

Dr. Bendel-Stenzel (left) and Dr. Georgieff wish James a cheerful "goodbye" from the neonatal unit. (March 8, 1996)

Primary nurses (left to right) Grace, Kari, and Bobbi check up on their one-year-old godsons after the boys were dedicated at Woodland Hills Church. (January, 1997)

CHAPTER 11

Home, Sweet Home

Summer 1996

I'm sure most first-time parents can relate to the overwhelming fear and uncertainty we felt when we brought our children home from the hospital. We now had two boys at home, and while they were nearly six months old, they were the size of newborns. James now weighed nearly eight pounds, but Henry weighed less than six. Suddenly there were no nurses or doctors at the bedside. The boys were now officially Catherine's and my responsibility.

I don't know who learns more during the infancy stage, the child or the parent. As the boys grew and developed, we as parents were learning right alongside them. They learned how to make sounds to communicate, roll over, grasp objects, and feed themselves. We as parents learned how to interpret their sounds and wants, feed and diaper crying babies, and meet the physical demands of caring for two premature infants. The learning never ends; each year brings new challenges and new learning opportunities.

Henry and James came home with some particular health concerns related to their prematurity. Both required apnea monitors, small devices that register the babies' breathing. The monitor is hooked up to electrodes that are placed on the baby's chest while he is sleeping. If the child stops breathing, the alarm sounds.

In the NICU we had been trained to operate and read the apnea monitor. The instructors taught us that if the alarm goes off, we should calmly go over to the baby and see if he is breathing. We were told to wait until the alarm had sounded for ten seconds; then if the baby is not breathing, we should gently nudge him, reminding him to breathe. We were not to run in and startle or wake the baby.

One night shortly after his homecoming, James' alarm sounded. Catherine and I both jumped out of bed. I dashed into his room, ran over to his crib and started calling very loudly, "James, James, are you all right?" I shook his shoulder lightly to awaken him.

Catherine walked in calmly behind me and reminded me, "Jon . . . Jon, we are supposed to wait 10 seconds; don't wake him." James did wake up crying, and yet his alarm continued to sound. Catherine, who had taken time to put on her glasses, looked at the monitor and started to laugh. In my near-sightedness, I could barely make out the orange glow of the blinking warning: "Low Battery." We had forgotten to plug in the monitor and its battery had worn down. Needless to say, I got to stay up with our crying baby while my calm, loving wife went back to sleep.

Henry came home on multiple medications. We set up the "Westby Pharmacy" on a butcher block cart in our kitchen. Catherine made up a chart which told what medication was needed at what time and in what dosage. Most of these meds were prescribed because of his chronic lung disease or *bronchopulmonary dysplasia* (BPD). He was on *diuretics*, including Diuril® and Lasix®, to decrease the fluid build-up in his lungs, and he was on two medications to replenish the electrolytes lost by his kidneys due to the diuretics. Both boys needed to be *nebulized* from time to time, a procedure which involved having them breathe in *albuterol*, a medically-treated mist, to open up the bronchi, enabling them to breathe easier. Some of Henry's medications had to be given every four hours, so we had to waken him during the middle of the night.

Because the boys were so small, they were able to consume only about two ounces per feeding. In order to get enough calories per day, they had to be fed every two to three hours, even at night. Once Henry was wakened, he was a much tougher child to get back to sleep; he wanted to be held and rocked. Some nights, when he absolutely refused to go back to sleep, we would take shifts rocking him. Around three or four in the morning Catherine would stumble into the bedroom, bleary-eyed, exhausted with a crying baby on her shoulder and pass him off to me for a two- or three-hour shift. Catherine would be asleep before her head hit the pillow. I admit it—my wife did the vast majority of this middle-of-the-night duty since I had to get up in the morning to go to work. Over a long period of time, this grueling schedule can be exhausting.

"I cried every single day," Catherine answers when asked for her most vivid memories of the boys' earliest weeks at home. She had the monstrous task of feeding, medicating, and nurturing our sons all hours of the day and night. My wife is strong-willed, and she takes pride in being a good mother. But she could also be stubborn. She was James' and Henry's mother; she would take care of them herself. After watching hospital staff care for her boys for nearly six months, Catherine wanted this time to bond with her babies. Her pride many times prevented her from asking for help. Our families' and friends' frequent offers of assistance were politely refused.

Because Henry came home on oxygen, we had hoses running throughout the house. A large oxygen tank was set up in our front entry way; one hose ran up stairs and another ran through the main floor. We also had a portable oxygen tank and hose for Henry whenever we took him outside. With all these monitors, oxygen tanks, hoses, nebulizers, bassinet, special preemie formula and medications, we had our own mini NICU right in our home.

Henry and James had frequent visits to the pediatrician, ophthalmologist, and cardiologist, in addition to checkups at the NICU Follow-up Clinic. It seemed as though every week they had one or two doctor appointments. Catherine would pack up the boys, carry two at a time in car seats, sling the diaper bag over one shoulder and Henry's portable oxygen tank over the other, and load everything into our roomy Honda Civic. Then off she'd go.

A home health care nurse, provided by Fairview-University Medical Center, visited weekly during the boys' first six months at home. She checked their heights, weights, medications, and general condition and answered Catherine's questions. These visits gave Catherine great reassurance.

Preemies who have BPD are very susceptible to colds and infections in their first few years. Henry and James were no exception. Regarding their health and development, it often seemed like the boys took two steps forward, then one step back. In February of 1997, Henry developed a bad case of pneumonia and had to be hospitalized for three nights at Fairview-University Medical Center. The pneumonia caused him to be dehydrated and he dropped weight he could ill afford to lose. He was put on an IV and bed rest.

This was a very sad time for our family. Henry had been home from the hospital for over eight months and until now had had no readmittance to the hospital—much to everyone's surprise. Doctors told us that most BPDers are rehospitalized several times during their first year. Catherine had to somehow keep the family together again. I was in the middle of teaching and another hockey season when this took place. James was not allowed into Henry's hospital room. Catherine felt she needed to be in two places at once—in the hospital with Henry and back at home with James.

During the day, while Catherine went to the hospital, one of our parents would stay with James. In the late afternoon, Catherine returned home. After I was done teaching and coaching for the day, I would spend time with Henry at the hospital before going home for the night.

The hardest part for both Catherine and me was leaving Henry at nights. This tiny, sick, year-old child was left with strangers in an unfamiliar place. It was obvious by the look of fear in Henry's eyes when one of us would leave that he was scared. Catherine and I have since said that if we had to do it all over again, one of us would have spent the nights up there with him. Henry did get better and he came home to his brother who missed him.

About a month after Henry's hospitalization, all four of us got hit with the 24-hour stomach flu. First James got sick—vomiting, diarrhea, the whole works. Before we knew it, I was bent over the toilet, spilling out my guts. Within a few hours Catherine, and finally

Henry, succumbed. All four of us were incredibly sick to the point of being barely able to function. All Catherine and I could do was lie on the boys' bedroom floor, taking turns running into the bathroom. We heard the boys cry and scream, but there was nothing we could do for them. We did not have the physical strength to assist them. I managed to phone my mother to ask her to deliver ginger ale and *Pedialyte®* to our back porch. I instructed her not to enter the house. Catherine and I both were shocked and saddened at our inability to help our sick children. It frightened us. Luckily, it was all over by the next day and we were soon on our way to recovery.

Another contributing factor to all our household chaos was our large black lab, Sam. Catherine and I had had Sam for over six years. She was a great dog, but with the arrival of our sons and the hours we spent away from home while the boys were in the hospital, she had grown very lonely. When the boys were about a year old, we realized we were going to have to give her away. In a very unfortunate and sad situation, she was diagnosed with a failing liver just the day after we gave her to our friends. I felt obligated to have her put to sleep. Both James and Henry, even though they were home with our dog for only a short while, bring her up in conversations. Often James prays for "Sam, our dog who died, who's up in heaven."

The financial burden of having premature children can be draining. I am very grateful that our health insurance covered the incredibly high cost of the boys' stay in the hospital. But once the boys were home, we found ourselves financially unable to keep up with the multiple co-pays, prescriptions, and medical devices that were necessities for our sons' health and development. The cost of the oxygen and tubing was $500 per month and was not covered by our health insurance. We were forced to swallow our pride and apply for Medical Assistance. Catherine remembers feeling humbled and embarrassed as she stood in line the first time at the Ramsey County Human Services Building. Though I knew we needed the help, the idea of assistance—welfare—did not sit well with my pride. We had to remind ourselves that this was temporary and that the services were for the health of our sons. We remained on Medical Assistance for 18 months.

As difficult as these first few months were, we soon began relishing the simple pleasures of being parents of twins. We proudly showed them off, tucked into their double stroller, during our family walks through the neighborhood. The neighbors' exclamations—"Oh, you have twins!"—brought smiles to our faces.

Our home entertainment now was listening to the boys babble and coo and watching them reach for objects and roll around on the floor. Most nights before we turned in, my wife and I would take one last look at our sleeping boys as they snuggled in their shared crib.

One of my earliest and fondest memories of the boys being home was of bottle-feeding the two of them on the couch: two babies feeding and two heads on my lap. Once they became strong enough to hold their own bottles, this position allowed me to massage their heads.

As the boys grew and developed, our house kept going through changes also. When they first came home, our house was filled with medical devices plus all the traditional infant toys: rattles, mobiles, pacifiers, baby swing, bouncy chair, infant seats and stuffed animals.

After a few months, the boys no longer were on monitors or oxygen. Eventually they started becoming mobile; our house, and the toys they played with, changed along with them. Now we had to put up gates, and move pictures and other breakables. The boys loved little stuffed animals, small balls, pots and pans, and books. By their second birthday our sun room had been turned into a miniature kitchen/work area with toy oven and sink, workbench for pounding and sawing, and several other pieces of equipment the grandmas and grandpas purchased to fill up our little house.

We set up a play area on our large back deck; here the boys first learned to pedal their little tricycles. On hot summer days we would put out their plastic wading pool and fill it with water. The boys loved to set their little slide in it and slide into the water. They preferred to play on the deck rather than the lawn because, from early on, they hated the feel of grass. We still laugh about an earlier summer when the boys were not yet walking. If we set the boys down on the grass, they would both lie on their backs, lift up their arms and legs, and flail away in unison. They reminded us of two turtles flipped over onto their shells.

In the spring of 2000 we decided we needed a larger home. That June we moved a total of three miles from our old two-bedroom brick house to a slightly newer three-bedroom home. Not only is this new house larger, but our yard is much more child-friendly with a white picket fence surrounding it.

Moving day was exciting. Before we filled the truck, James and Henry got to run up and down the truck ramp and play inside the large empty trailer; they had a ball. They also carried some of their own belongings out to the truck. Today our back yard is strewn with toys for five-year olds: a plastic wading pool, bicycles with training wheels, roller blades, bats and balls, shovels and rakes.

As our boys and our house have changed, one thing that has remained constant is the loving and nurturing that Catherine brings to our home. No matter how many toys the boys have, or how large a house we have, they will always know that their mom and dad love them.

CHAPTER 12

Are Those Boys Twins?

In five short years, I have watched with wonder as my two sons have developed both physically and emotionally. I am in awe as to how these two little boys, who started out so small, continue to flourish. They constantly surprise me with what they can do, not with what they can't do. Both physically and developmentally they have taken very different paths.

Henry was by far the sicker baby at birth. The standing joke while the boys were in the NICU was that if James had been a single birth, he would have received a lot more concern and attention. Even though he also was very small and sick, compared to his brother he was doing remarkably well. As we went through one crisis after another with Henry, James' health and welfare were taken for granted.

Physically, James has grown steadily, adding inches each year. Henry's growth has been slower, and he tends to grow in spurts. Months go by with no sign of growth, and then all of sudden—seemingly overnight—he'll shoot up an inch or two. Both boys are still under-sized for their age; however James is about three inches taller than Henry and outweighs him by six pounds. This is a significant difference at their heights.

Because of our sons' size difference, strangers often ask us, "Are those boys twins?" I don't know how many times I have been asked that question at a neighborhood park, but it has been numerous. The boys strongly resemble each other and they often dress alike. For the first two or three years I would answer yes to these inquiries, and follow with a lengthy history on the boys and their early arrival and Henry's heart surgery. I soon tired of feeling as though I had to explain their differing sizes. Now whenever anyone asks if the boys are twins, I answer with a cool, "Yes." Often my response is followed by a lengthy uncomfortable silence. This is just my way of saying, "Yes, my sons are small, and one is smaller than the other—but, so what!" Maybe this is why I don't make more friends at the park.

Throughout the boys' early years, Fairview-University Medical Center has done an excellent job of following them, tracking their physical and cognitive development. Probably the most important of all of their different doctors' appointments have been the NICU follow-up visits with Dr. Georgieff. These visits always turn into a reunion; we see some of James' and Henry's NICU doctors, nurses, and occupational therapists. At these sessions, doctors measure the boys' height, weight, and head size. Then they complete an assessment of their motor and cognitive development, using tests such as *The Bayley Scales of Infant Development* and the *Stanford-Binet Intelligence Scale, Fourth Edition.*

The medical staff uses this information to help identify certain potential disabilities and/or developmental problems that may arise; they then recommend to the parents the appropriate services and therapies for that child.

Catherine and I have felt these follow-up visits have been beneficial not only to Henry and James, but also to us. These follow-ups have allowed us to track their development, ask questions of the doctors and nurses, and gain knowledge and confidence in how we go about approaching the boys' development and education.

In addition to the NICU visits, the boys have regular appointments with their pediatrician where their height and weight are tracked. Catherine and I both have felt at some point overwhelmed with all the statistics and measurements. As parents we worry. Are they growing, developing? What does that score on his mental capabilities mean? We would love to have had two healthy, full-term babies that developed on schedule. Catherine and I have found that it is hard not to compare our children to others. We have learned that the path we walk with premature children is a different path from that walked by parents with full-term healthy babies.

Catherine is also saddened by the fact that she did not complete her pregnancy to the full nine months. *Star Tribune* writer Kay Miller points out that Catherine is not alone in these feelings of sorrow: " Statistics do not reflect the often unspoken, but deeply felt dream for many women....to finish a pregnancy, to nurse a baby, to look at a developmental chart and see one's child progressing blessedly on schedule" (Miller, 2001).

In the summer of 2000, NICU doctors determined that they did not need to see James again. His physical and cognitive development had progressed to the point that he had caught up with other boys his age. They still wanted to monitor Henry, but he no longer needed a yearly check-up. They asked to see him again after he completed kindergarten.

Henry and James have each developed their own distinct personalities. Henry is more stubborn and defiant; he is much more ready to say "No!" He tends to be more independent and can play by himself or with James; it doesn't really matter to him. He is also the one who, if he wants to play or experiment with something like daddy's saw or drill, just helps himself. If one interacts with Henry long enough, one can really see the fighting spirit in him that has carried him so far in his short little life.

James, on the other hand, is our rule follower. He is always ready to tattle on his brother, or me, for that matter. He is the one who says things like, "Daddy, Henry's playing in the dirt and Mommy said we can't with our new shoes on." Or, "Mommy, Henry said 'Poop' and that's not nice." James is also Mister Social, always talking, entering into adults' conversations. He is less independent than Henry; he almost always wants Henry to play with him. James asks permission for everything. "Can I color?" "Daddy, can I play with your screw driver?" He also has perseverance; he recently sat down with a very difficult puzzle of the United States and proceeded to spend a half-hour putting it all back together again.

James has assumed a big brother role toward Henry, looking out for his older but smaller twin. Catherine and I get frustrated because James sometimes dominates over Henry. He answers questions for Henry or takes over certain physically-challenging tasks for him. On occasion he even bosses Henry around. What contributes to this problem is that often Henry is happy to sit back and have someone else do his work for him. We many times have to remind James that we are not talking to him, and that Henry can answer for himself or do the task independently.

With the exception of Buzz Lightyear, the toys they choose also differ. Henry prefers to play with small figures, like Winnie the Pooh and Tigger; he uses his imagination to make up stories with these small characters. For their fourth birthday, they received a large container of Lincoln Logs. Henry doesn't care about building anything with the logs, but the set came with a tiny shopkeeper, a woman with a bucket, and some farm animals. He can spend hours with these little characters. Catherine and I laugh when he misplaces the little woman because he'll ask, "Where's my woman?"

With my smart-aleck humor I always answer, "I don't know, but there's mine," as I point to Catherine.

James prefers building things out of LEGOs, playing games such as Candy Land or High Ho Cherry-O, spelling words with letters, and riding his bike.

The eating habits of our boys also differ. James is our bread and dairy guy; he likes bread, rolls, bagels, cheese, yogurt, and ice cream. Henry, or "T-Rex" as we call him, eats meat of any kind: chicken, ground beef, sausage, bacon. His favorite cuts, however, are the more expensive: pork tenderloin, steak, and salmon fillet.

Due to Henry's small size and slow growth rate, his diet has been a concern since he was an infant. He has recently been tested for food allergies; the results show he is allergic to all milk, cod fish, and egg whites. This explains his aversion to all dairy products.

Henry also has always had a reflux problem, many times throwing up his formula as a baby. The hospital dietition prescribed adding *Thick-it®* to his formula to try to help him keep it down. He still occasionally struggles with this condition; and although we take Henry's reflux problem seriously, his timing for throwing up is legendary in our family. Christmas Eve, weddings, pool parties, Grandpa Hank's 90th birthday—none have been spared from Henry's puking. The problem concerns Catherine and me because Henry needs every calorie he consumes.

When the boys were babies, we many times lay them down in front of a mirror; we would laugh as we watched them admiring themselves. When they grew old enough to say their names, we would hold one up in front of the mirror and ask, "Who is that?" James would always say, "Henry," and Henry would answer, "James." Each would give us a puzzled look as we tried to explain to him that it was he, and not his brother.

Identifying early pictures also confused them. If only one of them was in a picture, either boy thought it was his brother and not himself. I don't think they fully realized the fact that they were twins and that they looked a lot alike until after their third birthday.

Like many sets of twins, Henry and James are best friends. If we ask one of them who his best friend is, each of them answers, "Henry" or "James." They do play and get along exceptionally well, and they both have vivid imaginations. It is a great joy to watch them chase each other through the dining room and living room, pretending to be Buzz Lightyear or Batman or a dinosaur. They both enjoy camping, fishing, and hiking. Recently they took swimming lessons together.

The boys have shared a crib or bed for most of their five years. When they first came home from the hospital, they were so small that they slept together crosswise in one crib. After they outgrew that, we put them in separate cribs butted up against each other. When they turned three we put them in separate toddler beds on opposite sides of the room, but every morning when we came in to wake them, the boys were sleeping together, snuggled in Henry's bed. After one week of this, we just pushed their beds together, creating one larger bed and they slept together. Now in our new home the boys have bunk beds, but because they are only five years old, they sleep together on the bottom bunk. We have told them that when they turn six, one of them can move up to the top bunk. The boys still take baths together, splashing water on each other and fighting over the bath toys.

Another sure sign that our boys are twins is that within a one-year period, both boys, on separate occasions, had to make trips to the emergency room to receive stitches in their heads. James was catapulted off our water bed, head first into a radiator. I hate to admit it (although Catherine never lets me forget), but it was my fault. I was wrestling both boys, and did a cannon ball onto the bed, only to watch James fly away. There was blood all over. I freaked out more than James did. The gash required eight stitches right down the middle of his forehead. He still has a thin scar to prove it. Henry received his head wound when James pushed him backwards into a radiator. Instead of the traditional method of stitches, Henry's wound was glued shut with liquid stitches.

How Henry and James communicate or whether they do talk to each other—away from mom and dad—has been a curiosity to me. Recently, James told me that Henry wanted a puppy. I asked, "Oh really? When did he tell you that?"

James' answer was: "Last night in bed." When I asked him if he and Henry often talked in bed, he answered, "Yes." I then told him that I had never heard them talking after bed time. He answered, "That's because we whisper." I jokingly told Catherine that I'd like to sneak a tape recorder into their room some night.

Soon after the boys were born, Catherine decided that she was going to stay home with the boys and not go back to work. It was a decision that I fully supported. We both come from families in which the mother stayed home for some years to raise children. To be honest, I think Catherine would have stayed home even if we had had a single, healthy child. I feel that young children need a parent to stay home. It does not have to be the mother, but there cannot be anything in a parent's life more important than the love and welfare of that child. No job or career can outweigh the importance of raising a child. Financial security has to take a back seat to love and emotional security. In our house, it is easy to

105

see the benefits of a stay-at-home mother and how much the boys gain from Catherine's presence. Both Henry and James are loving, happy boys.

In the spring of 1998 I made a professional choice to give up coaching hockey. It was really not that hard of a decision. I wanted to spend more time with my sons, and I wanted them to be able to spend more time with their father. I had found out in those first three years of their life, that as much as I loved coaching hockey, I missed my sons more. During the hockey season, which runs from early November to the end of February, I got to see the boys only on the weekends. I taught during the day and then coached late afternoons and evenings. I rarely got home before 7 or 8 at night; the boys would already be in bed. Catherine, in her usual caring way, encouraged me to keep coaching, knowing full well I might miss it once I left the sport. I am happy to say that I made the right decision; time with my sons is valuable. I am home almost every day by 4:30 or 5 and get to chase them around in our backyard or in the house. I believe it has been good for my sons, also, as they have begun to grow into young boys.

Catherine and I believe that our decision to spend more time with our sons in their early years has been the right choice. Neither one of us wants to be saying when the boys are grown and out of the house, "I sure wish I had stayed home and spent more time with our boys." Henry and James are going to be kids only once, and Catherine and I want to be there for it.

106

CHAPTER 13

Happily Ever After

"Marriage is like running a marathon, not a sprint." Being a runner, and the amatuer psychologist I always pretend to be, this is what I tell my friends and colleagues. A good marriage is going to last a long time, hopefully a lifetime. It takes work to make it last.

Having children is the most wonderful experience in the world. The bond between a parent and a child is unlike any other. With the addition of children to a marriage, the family is now complete. It is hard to explain the joy of being a family; I like to look at it as the joy and happiness of the love I have for my wife, multiplied 100 times over. The love and happiness of two spreads and now is shared by four. But despite all the joys of family life, it can also be very difficult.

As our family has evolved and changed, so has the love Catherine and I feel for each other. Catherine's and my marriage right now is the strongest it has ever been. We both joke about how young and naive we were when we first married. Catherine was 21 and I was 22. We loved each other then, or thought we did. We have been fortunate in that, over time, our marriage has grown stronger.

Many times, after the children are born, the relationship between the husband and wife gets put on the back burner. With the early arrival of our sons and all the difficulties we went through in those first two years, our marriage suffered. In our 12 years of marriage, the 7th year was by far the hardest. We went through a six-month period where I did not know if this marriage was going to last. This is still a very difficult time for Catherine and me to talk about, even though it was over four years ago. The problems in our marriage started soon after the boys' first birthday. Because of their delayed development, neither one of them was walking or was even very mobile yet.

Catherine was busy tending these two little guys, dragging them all over town to doctors' visits, doing piles of laundry, and trying to keep up with housework and cooking. My busy time of year was always November to March, the hockey season. I taught physical education during the day and then coached hockey into the early evenings. By the end of each day, my wife and I were both just shot.

It was about this time that I started feeling as though I was of little use at home. I selfishly felt as though Catherine had no time for me. I found myself, instead of running home to my wife and sons, arranging to go have a beer after practice with my assistant coaches to discuss strategy. Or I would meet some colleagues from school for a drink after work.

As my problems with my marriage increased, so did my dependence on my friends. There were three individuals who helped me through this rough period: my friend Rick, whom I have known since sixth grade; my running buddy and former boss, Keith; and a colleague named Kris. These friends allowed me to ramble on at great length and offered me sound advice and encouragement. I would meet Keith or Rick for coffee, or maybe a run. They would listen to me and then tell me how lucky I was to have someone as loving and caring as Catherine. They always brought up the twins. "You're telling us you are going to leave those boys without a father?" Working to save my marriage was very hard for my friends because over the years they had developed strong relationships with Catherine. Rick is also a godfather to our sons.

I received valuable advice from Kris, who is a runner like myself; once or twice a week we would run together after work. Being female, she saw things from a different point of view than Rick or Keith. Her words always centered around the topics of love and relationships. Despite the counseling of these friends, I was unable to remedy my unhappiness at home.

There was never one specific thing that I can put my finger on which led to our problems. I feel we just lost touch with each other and I exacerbated the situation. We hit bottom one day in early April of 1997. After a couple months of almost no communication from me, Catherine asked, "What is wrong? You don't say anything, and all you do is mope around the house!" This was not the first time she had confronted me about my silence.

I'm not sure what prompted me finally to answer her after weeks of saying nothing, but I said, "I'm not sure I want to be married to you anymore." I told her I needed to get away for a couple of nights to get my head on straight. This was not something she needed to hear at this point in our lives. In her usual loving and caring manner she said, "If that's what it takes to save this marriage, then by all means go."

Whenever I need to think, I require peace and solitude; I can't have any distractions. So I grabbed my backpack and hiking boots and headed up to the North Shore of Lake Superior. I can remember bits of this short two-day trip like it was yesterday. I started my hike in the rain and snow. I was cold and wet within the first five minutes. I hiked for two or three hours and found a place to set up my tent along the Superior Hiking Trail. I then climbed a high bluff with a view of Lake Superior and sat down in the rain and snow. I asked myself, "What am I doing, throwing away a beautiful and wonderful marriage? How can I leave my two adorable sons?" I wish I could say that I had an awakening on this bluff, but I did not. When I eventually climbed down, my thoughts were the same as when I had climbed up; I was doubting my love for Catherine and hers for me.

There were many signs that I should have picked up on at this point, directing me as to the grave mistake I was considering making. I was cold and wet from the rain and snow. I started my whisper-light camp stove; it blew up and everything within a two-foot radius was on fire—the stove itself, the ground, and fuel bottle. I tried to put out the flames, and I melted the only gloves I had on the trip. I got the fire out, but parts of my stove had melted, making it useless.

I soon became hungry, but I had almost nothing to eat that wouldn't require cooking. Needless to say, I spent a very uncomfortable night in my tent—cold, wet and hungry. I remember thinking to myself that this would be really funny to my friends if I ever told them about everything going wrong. I take pride in being an expert camper.

At the crack of dawn I packed up my tent and hiked back to the warmth of my car and drove home. That night Catherine and I had a very painful heart-to-heart talk; I shared with her all my doubts about our marriage. We talked more the next few nights after the boys were in bed. These conversations always involved tears from Catherine and shame from me.

We slowly and painfully started working our way out of this deep hole. We began making more of an effort to talk to each other. On occasions now we have deep, long, hearfelt talks into late hours of the night.

The topics can vary—not only about our marriage, but about parenting, religion, school, and more. We both really enjoy going off on these long discussions.

I remember finally telling myself, "Jon, you've got it great; you need to wake up and start working on this marriage and see just how wonderful your wife and children are." It took time, months for that matter, but the troubles we went through brought us closer together. I know that every year that goes by I seem to love Catherine more and more. I see all her great attributes: love of her children, family and friends; spirituality; openness; compassion and humor. Catherine is one of these rare individuals who goes out of her way to make sure other people's well-being is taken care of before her own. She is constantly giving of her time. One day she cooks dinner for a family in need; the next day she gives someone a ride. Her friends know she is one individual who can always be depended on. These are just some of her qualities that, as I grow older and more mature, I have come to love and admire.

One reason I think some couples have marriage problems is that men and women seem to think and reason differently. Catherine and I do not process information in the same way. We had a conference with Henry's and James' learning readiness teachers in the fall of 2000. At this meeting Henry's teachers suggested that we get him assessed for the disability *MMI* which stands for mildly mentally impaired. My wife and I were both familiar with the term; I have taught

112

for over 12 years in the Minneapolis Public School System and have had MMI students in my classes. When this term is used for the first time in relation to your own child, it is quite devastating. Catherine cried during this conference, but I, being the strong male type, waited until I was alone.

That night Catherine wanted to talk about what we should do. She asked what my feelings were about this new development in Henry's education. My answer was that I needed a day or two to think about it. I wanted to check with some of my colleagues before I decided what we should do. My wife wanted us to express right then and there our deep emotional feelings about what had taken place that day during the conference. I wanted to get analytical and obtain facts and statistics to back up our decision—whatever it might be.

After two days of gathering information from the social worker, special education teacher, and speech clinician at my school, I was finally ready to talk with Catherine about what I thought was best for Henry. We had a wonderful, productive, intimate discussion. After we came to some conclusions about what approach to take for Henry's future education, Catherine explained to me why it had been painful for her the previous two days.

That first night after the conference, she wanted to hear my thoughts and feelings, but she also needed someone to listen to hers. She needed to bare her soul to someone, and she wanted me—her husband—to be that person.   I was too busy preparing to defend my position that Henry was not **MMI**; I forgot about my wife and her needs.   In happy, loving marriages, there has to be some give and take to allow both husband and wife to have their needs met.   Luckily for me, Catherine is very tolerant and loving.

I have empathy for parents of small children.   I know how much energy it takes to raise kids.   It is hard to give time and attention to a spouse when one is feeding and changing babies 16 hours a day.   There is just no time or energy left at the end of the day to give to a partner.   I have a soft spot in my heart, especially for parents who give birth to babies who are premature or have other medical crises.   For these parents "...the delight in having kids has been ground smooth by the daily wear-and-tear of medical crises, stays in the newborn intensive care unit, colic, feeding problems, developmental delays and financial and emotional stress" (Miller, 2001).

As husbands and wives, we really have to try to make time for each other.   This is not always easy.   I have learned how important it is, for the sake of the marriage, to allow for some quality time for just the husband and wife—perhaps to go to a movie or dinner. In our case, as the boys got a little older, it did get easier.

We have also come to realize the importance of our own certain independence.   One cannot parent 24 hours a day, 365 days a year without needing a break.   As parents we now know we cannot spend every waking minute with our sons. We need to continue our individual lives as well if we want to be contributing members to our community. Catherine enjoys her time with friends: to walk, shop, go for coffee, volunteer, or even join together for the occasional "girls' night out."

Catherine is very accommodating, granting me time to run, bike, or ski almost daily. I have a love for the wilderness, inherited from my father, which I hope to pass on to my sons. When the pull of the great outdoors becomes too strong, I take off on my next adventure. With Catherine's blessing (actually I think she gets tired of me getting in her way during summer and winter vacations) I head north to canoe or cross-country ski in the Boundary Waters Canoe Area. A few summers I've humped a 50 lb. backpack up a rocky trail in the Montana wilderness. I am usually accompanied by one or more of my friends: Rick, Mark, or Mike—all fathers.

We have an almost boyish competitive nature about us. On these adventures, we push ourselves to the brink of exhaustion, trying to break the fragile psyche of one another. On more than one occasion I have ended up spread-eagle over a rock, throwing up due to dehydration or altitude sickness. My frailties always bring a smile to my friends' faces. In a primitive, nomadic way, these trips re-energize me and I feel I am a better father and husband because of them.

As Catherine's and my love for each other has grown, I have seen the positive effect this love has had on Henry and James. We have many times been told, even by complete strangers, how caring and loving our sons are. I need to thank her for sticking by my side when things got tough. As Catherine and I grow older together, I am more confident now than I have ever been about our relationship.

CHAPTER 14

Early Childhood
Special Education

Due to Henry's and James' prematurity and developmental delays, they have received special services since the time of their birth. In the NICU, an occupational therapist came in two to three times a week to give them a little exercise. She moved their arms and legs around, and made sure they were not always lying in the same position. Even more importantly, she observed both boys for signs of neurological or motor impairments.

When they came home from the hospital, both boys qualified for special education services through the St. Paul Public Schools. Fairview-University's staff social worker and the occupational therapist referred Catherine to our school system's Birth-to-3 Division. Catherine and I quickly became familiar with terms like *ECFE* (Early Childhood Family Education), *ECSE* (Early Childhood Special Education), *IEP* (individual education plan), *DD* (developmentally delayed), and

MMI (mildly mentally impaired). I am a teacher, and yet even I was surprised at the many services available to special-needs newborns through the public schools.

When the boys reached the age of nine months, a special education teacher, a physical therapist, an occupational therapist (or sometimes all three) began making weekly visits to our home. The teacher helped the boys with skills such as self-awareness and language development. The therapists worked on strengthening and building the core muscles in their upper bodies to enable them to sit unaided and to roll over. They had the boys do pushing exercises as well as grasping and pulling on blankets or small ropes. The doctors had not yet ruled out the possibility that Henry may have cerebral palsy; the therapist closely monitored him for discernable signs.

Catherine enjoyed these visits, not only because of the developmental purposes they served for Henry and James, but also for her own social interaction with other adults. The doctors had advised us to keep the boys at home as much as possible that first winter and not to bring them into crowds of people. Catherine always felt the visits of these professionals were over all too soon. They provided Catherine with companionship and the reassurance that she was on the right track in her care of these two preemies. I was working and rarely attended these sessions, but when I could be there, I noticed a bond between Catherine and the teachers. I could also tell that they thought Henry and James were something special.

In addition to the assessments made by the St. Paul Schools' Early Childhood Department, the boys' progress was monitored through visits to the University's NICU Follow-up Clinic. The report of one of Henry's early assessments reads as follows:

"On September 24, 1997, Henry was 21 months old, with a corrected age of 18 months. His height was 18 inches. His weight was 17 lbs., 5 oz. and his head circumference was 46 cm. When comparing these measurements with what is called the IHDP growth percentile for very low birth weight premature boys, his height and weight were below the 5th percentile, his head size was at the 25th percentile. His developmental scores from the administration of The Bayley Scales of Infant Development included a score of less than 50 on the mental development section, and on the motor development (section) a score of 51. These scores put him at an age equivalency of 11 months.

"Henry has made some nice changes in his gross motor skills in the last six months. He is stronger: moving in and out of sitting independently, crawling, standing, cruising along furniture and just beginning to stand alone for a few seconds."

These reports were beneficial in showing Henry's progress; they enabled Catherine and me to set educational goals. However, the reports also forced us to face the reality that, yes, our child had a developmental delay. That cold hard truth can leave a loving parent in anguish.

I often found myself getting frustrated as I watched our sons' peers reaching certain milestones—walking, being potty trained, catching a ball—long before our boys. I have a much harder time waiting patiently than my wife does. I must admit that in their own due time, when they were ready, the boys eventually mastered these important skills.

Our records of the boys' development verify this "alternate path we walk":

> James: 11 months —sits up with support; 18 months-— walks; 22 months —can speak the following words: cheese, shoe, mom, dad, and baby.
> Henry: 14 months —scoots backwards and gets stuck under furniture; 15 months —holds own bottle; 17 months —sits up independently; 22 months-—cruises along furniture and pulls himself up to standing; 24 months —walks!!

The joke in our family is that no one can tell Henry what to do or when to do it. We pleaded for him to remain calm in the womb; he kicked his way out early. We worked and worked with him, trying to get him to walk before his second birthday. Two days after his birthday, he stood up and walked across our living room. We feel he is telling us nonverbally, "I'll do it when I'm good and ready—not when you want me to! Quit bugging me!"

In the fall of 1998, on the recommendation of Henry's ECSE teacher and his occupational therapist, we enrolled him in a class that met two mornings a week at a nearby St. Paul Public School. Since this was an ECSE class, only special education students were enrolled. He would no longer be receiving special education services at home.

Henry's first day of school was difficult for all of us. He was scared being dropped off at this strange new school with unfamiliar teachers. Leaving her 2½-year-old son, trusting his care to strangers, was both sad and frustrating for Catherine. James was confused and a little disheartened that Henry got to go to school but he didn't. I was worried about everyone; I just hoped we would all make it through this first day.

We had bought Henry a new backpack for school. Catherine packed it with diapers, a change of clothes, and school supplies. As a family we drove to J.J. Hill School. When we all got out of our car, Catherine put the pack on Henry's back, posing him for a first-day-of-school photo. Because he was still small and somewhat weak, the weight of the backpack started to pull him backwards, forcing him to back-pedal until he nearly fell over. Try as we might, we could not adjust the pack to fit him, so Catherine had to carry his bag into the school. All of us, especially James, had a good laugh.

Henry had a functioning educational label of DD (developmentally delayed). Due to Henry's size and prematurity, his delays tended to fall into two categories: speech/language and motor skills. The class enrolled just six students, some of whom were classified as DD and some who were autistic. Henry started the school year slowly, but in the spring he really flourished. This established a pattern that we would continue to see with Henry in each school year.

The environment of this class was nurturing. Though his language and verbal skills were very delayed, Henry was the most verbal child in this group; so in the spring of that year, after consulting with Henry's doctors from the NICU and his ECSE teachers, we decided that Henry would benefit more from a mainstream pre-school. We wanted Henry to interact with other regular education pre-school children and hoped that the more verbal environment would enhance his use of language.

For the 1999-2000 school year we enrolled both Henry and James in Tiny Tots, a West St. Paul private pre-school. We chose this school because our nieces had attended the program and we knew the teachers to be caring and child-centered. This class was a mix of 3½-to 5-year-olds, all sizes and developmental levels. Henry and James were the smallest in this class, Henry most noticeably.

I observed this delightful class a few times and noticed the wide range of skills within the group. Some children could already print their names or draw a complete picture. Some could tie their own shoes. Then there were others, like Henry and James, who were just learning to hold a pair of scissors or take off their shoes.

Henry was treated like a little brother. Many in the class, including James, looked out for his welfare. A couple of the girls in this class went out of their way to help Henry, escorting him to the story circle, getting his crayons or scissors, or inviting him to join their "tea parties." This was a Catch-22. It was really cute the way these young kids took Henry under their wing and protected him, but we wanted him to be able to do these things for himself. Henry is smarter than a lot of us give him credit for; he is very happy to have someone else do his work for him. The teachers were well aware of this and soon, with our blessing, they insisted Henry get his own supplies or find his way into line.

Henry's development took a path very similiar to the previous year. He started off slowly in the fall, gradually built up speed over the winter months, and finished strong in the spring. We decided his slow starts were due to the unfamiliarity of the new routines, his being slightly scared, and his general developmental delays. During that school year Henry continued to receive his speech and occupational therapy through the St. Paul Public Schools. Every Wednesday, when

Catherine took both boys to an ECFE class in our neighborhood, Henry met with his specialists.

In James' first year of pre-school at Tiny Tots, he thrived. He participated in group activities, including singing and story time. He slowly learned how to take turns and share with his peers, and he got better at following directions. He mastered the basic academics appropriate for his age: he learned his colors and shapes and could count to 20. His fine motor skills of cutting and writing lagged behind, but slowly started to emerge. Most important of all, he really enjoyed "going to school."

Five months after the boys' fourth birthday, James was exited from special education services. He had made steady developmental progress and there was no further need for him to be seen by an occupational therapist or special education teacher. I know the benefits of early intervention and of ECSE, but I rejoiced when James outgrew these services. Watching James progress and develop despite such a precarious start to life brings a lump to my throat.

Although we were happy with the progress Henry had made at Tiny Tots, especially in the spring, we began to look for a different placement for that fall. We hoped to find a program that was closer to our home, would meet at least three times per week, and would enroll both our sons. The situation resolved itself when Henry's case manager recommended an Early Childhood Special Education/Learning Readiness program through the St. Paul Public Schools. The class would enroll 16 prekindergartners, six of whom would be classified as special education students. The other 10 students would be mainstream. Our boys could both be in this class.

In the fall of 2000, at the age of $4\frac{1}{2}$, Henry started his third school. The organization of this set-up was ideal; an early childhood teacher and a special education teacher worked together in one room, assisted by a full-time aide. The occupational therapist and speech clinician also came in several hours a week. The class never filled to capacity, so the boys received a lot of individual attention from the adults. It was a great year for both Henry and James.

One of the best aspects of this program was the extensive communication between the teachers and parents. Teachers held a conference for both Henry and James early in the school year. In the late fall, we had an IEP meeting at our house concerning Henry. Between the winter and spring we had three more conferences or meetings. These were in addition to the day-to-day communication between Catherine and the teachers.

Through the experience of that school year, I also learned how teachers and parents can work together to meet the needs of their children. It was at Henry's fall IEP conference that his teachers first brought up the idea of having him reassessed, to change his disability label from DD to a more specific label of MMI (mildly mentally impaired).

Having been a teacher for the past 12 years, I have sat in on many IEP meetings involving MMI, autistic, cerebral palsy, or other disabled students. Now, as the parent, I found myself on the other side of the table. It was much different here; it was my own child and his future being planned. I found that I could not, and did not want to, remove myself emotionally from the parent's vantage point. Catherine took the idea of the MMI label really hard and cried during this conference.

Henry's teachers—including the OT, speech clinician, and social worker—had his best interest at stake. They thought that by labeling him MMI, his chances for receiving appropriate services in kindergarten would be improved. The developmentally delayed label is more generally used at the early childhood level and is not used after a child reaches the age of seven.

Catherine and I knew Henry was behind developmentally, especially in the areas of language and both fine and gross motor development. But we were hopeful that he would make measurable gains during the second half of the school year.

After consulting with some of my colleagues and the NICU doctors, Catherine and I discussed our options. We decided to go in a slightly different direction as far as labeling Henry and yet ensuring he would get the services he needs. Neither of us felt the MMI label was appropriate for Henry at this early age. With his prematurity and his complications at birth, we argued,

Henry fell into the category OHI (other health impairment). We obtained a letter from his doctors at the University of Minnesota, explaining all the problems Henry had at birth, including his intraventricular brain bleeds, lung disease, and heart surgery.

When we presented our rationale for the OHI label, Henry's team of teachers showed the depth of their care for our son. They did not get upset or feel slighted because Catherine and I disagreed with their recommendation. They took our lead and dug up more information for us about OHI. They invited the district MMI specialist to come observe Henry and to help rule out the MMI label. Most importantly, they continued to show both Henry and James the care and tenderness that only an ECSE teacher can. Henry's entire team of educators gave this plan their OK and drew up a new IEP. In the spring, the lead teacher organized a transitional meeting for us, including the teams from Henry's learning-readiness program and the special education team from the school we had selected for the boys' kindergarten.

Our entire family enjoyed working with this group of preschool teachers. The boys loved them, and both James and Henry benefited greatly from this school year. True to form, in the spring Henry showed his true colors and made some remarkable gains.

Choosing an appropriate placement for Henry for kindergarten was a concern for both Catherine and me. Nearing the end of his year at the Learning Readiness Program, we still had many more questions than answers in regard to his academic and functional level. The summer before kindergarten Henry could identify about half of the upper case letters, count to 20, say the ABCs, identify shapes, and sort by colors. His greatest weaknesses came in his gross and fine motor skills (writing, coloring, cutting), his social interaction with peers, and his ability to process information such as multiple-step directions.

Part of the problem is that Henry has not yet learned to transfer what he can do in the safe confines of our home to the larger unfamiliar classroom setting. While he could identify 20 upper case letters for us, he identified only 3 or 4 for his teachers.

The St. Paul Public Schools were very helpful. They offered suggestions, made contacts on our behalf, and set up tours of possible kindergarten sites. We toured three schools, two of which had special MMI programs. We finally settled on our neighborhood school, Groveland Park Elementary. It met many of the criteria we were looking for at the time: half-day kindergarten with special education support services available within a regular education setting. Both boys could attend, and yet be in different classrooms. Conveniently located in our neighborhood, the school has a strong reputation for academic excellence.

Through the boys' first few years of schooling, Catherine and I have met only the kindest and most diligent educators. They have been approachable, caring, and professional. It takes a special kind of person to be an early childhood teacher—loving, caring, patient. We thank them very much for helping enrich our sons' lives.

CHAPTER 15

Grandmas and Grandpas

Henry and James are very fortunate. They have two sets of loving, caring grandparents. As we have traveled along this journey the last five years, they have been there for us the entire way—praying, baby-sitting, changing diapers. I have been curious as to how the birth of their grandsons has affected their lives. Not wanting to be overly intrusive, I have never asked them— until now.

The following passages are edited and shortened versions of their beautiful and passionate responses.

Born into our Hearts

The story of the birth of Henry and James is worthy of remembering and retelling. It is a story of God's grace, doctors' and nurses' skills, and two people facing an unprecedented challenge in their young married life.   Other families have faced similar situations, but this happened to our family; this makes it highly personal and real.   We discovered as a family that life is filled with pathos and pain, uncertainties and mystery.   This event became for us an emotional roller-coaster ride.

In the underdevelopment of these infants' small bodies, our family witnessed total dependency.   Their very existence was reliant upon the wisdom and skills of doctors, the constant care and monitoring of nurses, medical machines, and the persistent love and prayers of Jon and Cate and a host of other people.

A multitude of hours were spent singing and talking, touching and rocking, hoping and praying. Great-grandpa Henry fondly recalls holding the babies in the hospital.   On one occasion, the nurse gave tiny Henry to great-grandpa Henry and then walked away, leaving him alone.   His surprise quickly turned to confidence and he was glad he could hold little Henry. His namesake has a special place in his heart.

Hands touching head and body.   Hands transmitting health and energy.   Voices softly singing over and over again songs, especially *Rock-a-bye-Baby*. Voices stimulating and strengthening kinetic energy. Parents kangarooing.   Skin-to-skin communication of life and vitality.   These simple human intimacies contributed to the twins' survival.   Maybe the birth of children is God's way of teaching us the importance of human contact and the need for intimacies.

Today they are thriving and growing under the leadership and modeling of their parents who see to it that the boys have many normal experiences. They entered our world under difficult conditions and today are learning how to survive and live. The twins were born into our hearts and now they benefit our lives. The grace of God continues.
(Grandpa Dick)

Henry's Rite of Spring

The chaplain approached us slowly in the hallway. We were told Henry was not getting oxygen to his lungs. Gently, he asked if we would like to go into the intensive care unit. We did, circling Henry's Isloette and joining hands. I fiercely wanted his survival, but also considered how impaired he might be. I began to give thanks for having at least one grandson. Henry, in retrospect beginning his incredible journey of determination, would have none of this "one" stuff. He survived the day!

Some days later I wrote the following poem as I recalled members of our family, all gathered around Henry with the chaplain in that moment. For me it became a vigil of hope and celebration, marveling at their being alive each day. James was the leader in this time of doubt and questioning, reaching each new stage, conquering each medical challenge. He led, and perhaps reached back his hand for his brother

Henry who was so unwilling to let go.   Although I
wrote this poem about Henry, after remembering the
feelings of that first day, James is certainly between
each line.

"HENRY"

He is stretched out full,
Glowing sunburn red.
His feet are so tiny,
A breathing mask on his head.

This infant here early,
Taken from her warm womb,
Exposed to this world,
To this cable strung room.

Yet handled so gently,
Each finger caressed,
Tender skin massaged
In this artificial nest.

There are so many tubes
And computer displays.
Hollow plastic that carries
each breath.   And we pray...

Alarms sound off
Unexpectedly!
Is his heart still beating?
Are his lungs still free?

In these hands so skilled
He's a miracle begun.
This first day of life,
His first morning sun.

We hold our thoughts closely
As we leave him in their care.
What we want, and what God sees
Is our halting, final prayer.

On Friday, January 12, the day before Henry would
have major surgery, Dinah and I went to Orchestra Hall
for a concert. A 1723 Stradivarius was used to perform
a beautifully calming Sibelius violin concerto. The
pounding percussion in *Rite of Spring* took my emotions
to Henry's heart, and a prayer that it would continue
with a strong beat. And the next day Henry defied the
odds in successful surgery.

Weeks later, shortly before Henry was discharged,
he and I listened in his hospital room to a Twins game.
They beat Baltimore while all the fans were hoping
Kirby's eye would heal.

(Grandpa Jim)

The Tortoise Beats the Hare

A team of six professionals in white smocks raced
towards me and slowed long enough for me to glance at
each one of the babies. I was grateful that they could

not linger longer. It was shocking to see what appeared in that moment to me two tiny birds resembling humans. Their lungs moved only with the aid of the hand-held pumps being manipulated by one of the team members. I prayed and prepared myself for the worst possible outcomes for them and for the strength Jon and Catherine would need.

I recall standing with the doctors by Catherine's bed. The team of medical staff shared what seemed to be a college course in physiology with us in a matter of fifteen minutes. Henry was not expected to live even another 45 minutes at that time.

Finally we were allowed a closer look at the babies. I looked at Henry. Before I could express my initial reaction of disbelief at the idea that someone would carelessly toss a 4 x 6 inch piece of bubble-wrap onto a fragile infant, someone immediately clarified that it was the lightest, best blanket for premature babies. Seeing him this way was a total numbing to my senses.

What followed that day remains a blurred experience. I recall leaving the hospital not knowing what to do or what I wanted to do. I only knew I needed to be alone amongst people who were totally oblivious to the crises in our lives, which crept along so slowly. The car took me to a shopping area where I rarely go. I walked aisles in search of something, not knowing what, but rather what *not*. When my eyes landed on a softly stuffed green turtle, I knew what I had been searching for, and tears washed away with the realization that it was a toy. No child should die without having had a toy that can be cuddled. This toy was symbolic to me. It meant that while the boys were impossibly tiny, we all know in the end that the Tortoise beat the Hare. This would be their mascot, mission statement and mantra. I went home and collapsed.

The following day, Henry was still with us. The toy turtles stood still as sentries atop their Isolettes. That evening, friends from church arrived at our home. Oh, the indescribable comfort of sharing, singing, praying and crying with friends.
(Grandma Dinah)

My Favorite Photos not Taken

Like many proud grandparents, I have taken dozens of photographs of our grandsons Henry and James. Posed and candid, indoor shots and outdoor, taken at family celebrations and during private moments. We joke that the first word either boy spoke was "Cheese!" It's impossible to capture every scene of a child's life in photos. There are many special moments in the history of our boys which live on only in my memory. Actual photographs capture just a fraction of a second. Photos of the mind can span moments and can capture tears and laughter. This is one of my favorite:

"FLYING HIGH"

On a crisp autumn day the sky is bright blue, just a few wisps of cloud passing by.   A golden-leafed branch arches over the Edgecumbe Park swing set. In matching tan fleece jackets and hats, my rosy-cheeked grandsons squeal in delight as I push first one and then the other.   One-two-three- Henry; one-two-three- James.   Over and over.   I am surprised at how high these little almost-two-year-olds want to fly.

"Fly high; up to the sky," I sing to them.

"To the sky," answers James.

"Ky," Henry echoes.

I had walked the boys the four blocks from their home to this park in their double stroller. Henry sitting in back, as always, and James in front.   James looked ahead, as if to be sure I followed the right route. Henry leaned over the side of the stroller, watching the wheels go around.   I so enjoyed these semi-regular outings with the boys because it was a special " Grandma time." I had offered to watch the boys for a couple hours so their mom could get some errands done, but it was really for my own benefit that I volunteered.   I was delighted when strangers smiled and exclaimed, "What cute little boys!   Are they twins?"

I tire of pushing the swings. "Let's go play in the sand now," I suggest. James agreeably raises his arms so I can lift him out.   Henry cries; he is not ready to quit.

Our photo albums grow thicker; we replace the framed photos on the mantle with new ones. But the most vivid pictures of the twins' history are the those I carry in my memory.

(Grandma Sandy)

At 11 months of age, the boys attend a Halloween party dressed as twin bears. (October, 1996)

By 14 months, Henry (left) and James have become mobile—scooting and crawling. They also drool in anticipation of cutting the first teeth. (January, 1997)

At 22 months, James (left) and Henry enjoy playing together on a teeter-totter. (September, 1997)

The 2½-year-old twins do their best Elton John impersonation. (May, 1998)

At a family gathering, 3½-year-old Henry prepares to pitch the ball. (June, 1999)

Below: In anticipation of Y2K, the Westby family rings in the New Millenium.
(December 31, '1999)

At the same park where his father learned to skate, James proudly demonstrates his skating ability. (January, 2000)

Below: James (left) and Henry enjoy Grand Marais Harbor while on a family vacation to the North Shore. (July, '2002)

CHAPTER 16

Celebration of Life

Henry and James have taught me the real importance of celebrating life. It was through their birth that I grew to understand just how precious and fragile life can be. In the past I had always believed that life was meant to be enjoyed; work some, play a lot, and if something makes you unhappy, don't do it. Because of Henry and James I have learned that there is much more to life than one big party.

The unconditional love of a child is the most wonderful celebration I have experienced. To have a child run up and wrap his arms around my neck, give me a hug, and yell "Daddy" is so intimate and unique that only other dads or moms would understand. A bad day at work can instantly be forgotten, a tired parent can be rejuvenated, what seems like a life-and-death matter can become trivial—all by the love and affection shown by a young child.

Catherine and I have had much to celebrate. We celebrated the day the boys were born. We celebrated when they both made it through the first night. During those early months, we celebrated every time a new milestone was passed: their first feedings, first bath, breathing without assistance of the ventilator, Henry's successful heart surgery. We celebrated and cried when we finally got to bring them home.

Once the boys were home, we would continue to mark joyous occasions: saying their first words; walking unassisted; learning to pedal their tricycles—all major reasons to shout out in joy.

The first time we really got to show off our boys was in the summer, shortly after Henry had come home from the hospital. We attended my cousin's wedding in northern Minnesota. The boys were only seven months old and were still so tiny; Henry weighed about six pounds, James about eight. We packed up the boys and a carload of their gear—including Henry's portable oxygen tank—and off we drove. It was our first weekend away as an entire family and it would be the first time my aunts, uncles, and cousins got to see the boys. I can remember how loving and excited many of them were to finally be meeting and holding the twins. The wedding itself was a grand celebration.

That fall we celebrated Henry's and James' first birthday. To show our joy and happiness, we had an open house; we invited all those who had prayed for the boys. It was our way of saying "thank you" to everyone who had shown us support and love over the previous year.

One group in particular that took a special interest in Henry and James were our parents' friends who were meeting the boys for the first time. I remember how excited they were to hold these babies they had heard so much about. Many of these people were already grandparents; they knew what Catherine and I were just now learning—that a child's life itself is meant to be celebrated and cherished. We topped off the day watching the babies stuff their faces full of cake, wearing more than they ate.

Catherine and I come from families that love to celebrate. Not a holiday or birthday or special event goes by without a party of food, family, and fun. My brother Steve, a gourmet cook, and his wife Joan often host our Westby family dinners. Early on, Henry and James found out that the entertainment at these parties involves singing, dancing, and story telling. Taking the lead from their very talented cousins, the boys have begun volunteering their talents for all to see and hear. James' talent is in the realm of comedy; he enjoys getting up in front of an audience to tell a joke, often telling the same joke to the same audience several times. His best one to date is: "What do you call a sleeping bull? A Bulldozer."

Henry is the really funny one, though, because he is always the first to volunteer; but when he faces his audience, he runs away yelling, " No!"

Catherine and I have many great memories of events that we have experienced as a family. We witnessed the Boundary Waters Canoe Area's "storm of the century" in 1999. Falling trees totaled our car (luckily we were not in it at the time) and left us marooned at a cabin. Our only mode of available transportation was by boat. We had to be rescued by my teaching partner Sara, who drove up in her Suburban after the roads were cleared. To this day, the boys talk about the wind and the tree that fell on our car.

The boys' fifth birthday celebration was another memorable event. Overnight our house became the home of *Buzz Lightyear®*. The only movie the boys have seen in a movie theatre is *Toy Story 2* , and they have been infatuated with Buzz ever since. Each boy received an *Original Buzz*; as one holds him up and flies him around, he says things like: "To infinity and beyond," or "Let's go—we have to rendezvous with star command!"

In addition, Henry received a *Room Guard Buzz*; when activated it sounds an alarm if someone walks by. James received a remote control car *(RC)* along with a Buzz driver. James became very good at operating this car, crashing it into every piece of furniture we own. They received Buzz sheets and pillow cases, and a few days later a small nerf Buzz basketball and hoop which we attached to their bunk beds. We ended the party with a Buzz Lightyear cake topped by two small plastic Buzz figures. Not surprisingly, these became Henry's favorite toys. It was official—Buzz was the new ruler in our house.

Now at the ripe old age of five, the boys are accomplished campers. Together our family celebrates the beauty of the great outdoors. Henry and James love sleeping in a tent, swimming, fishing, gazing at a fire, hiking, and their favorite—eating s'mores. I cannot wait until I take them on their first Boundary Waters canoe trip, as my father did with me and our family.

The boys recently completed their first set of swimming lessons. They made remarkable progress over a short two-week period. Catherine and I proudly watched them kick around the pool with their water wings on.

As important as these family celebrations were, we look back on two important public ceremonies as highlights in our history. In January of 1997 at a Child Dedication Service at our church—Woodland Hills— Catherine and I pledged to raise Henry and James as Christians. This service was very emotional from a spiritual standpoint, because so many members in the church knew of our struggles and had prayed for so long. Both our sets of parents attended, and so did the boys' godmothers—Kari, Bobbi and Grace—-their primary nurses from the NICU. One of the boys' godfathers, my buddy Ray, was also in attendance with his wife. Not surprisingly, Catherine cried at the dedication.

In the summer of 2000, Fairview-University Medical Center produced a video to be used as a fundraiser for the NICU. The film featured Henry and James as well as one other NICU graduate. We were eager to participate because we felt the hospital had done so much for our family. Catherine and I were interviewed for this video, and the boys were filmed playing in our new back yard. The interview brought back many emotional memories, and Catherine and I both cried at some point during the filming. The following February we were invited to the NICU's black tie gala where this video, titled *The Stork's Nest*, was shown. Catherine gave an eloquent and heartfelt speech to the aproximately 1,000 guests and dignitaries in attendance.

The celebrations of life are many. For me, the celebration of love among a family is the greatest and strongest of them all. I cannot go through an hour of my day without having some thought of my sons or my wife. This triggers a smile, a laugh, or maybe a tear, reminding me just how lucky I am.

CHAPTER 17

Hopes and Dreams

All parents have hopes and dreams for their children. Catherine and I are no different. Often I think of our sons' futures, especially Henry's. Maybe I am too optimistic about James, but I see how he learns, asks questions, solves problems, and interacts with others. His progress these past few years leaves me feeling confident that he will continue to thrive.

It is Henry that I mainly worry about. I see him walking, teetering along on top of a fence, and I'm just waiting to see on which side of the fence he's going to fall.

Will his attention span increase? Will his problem-solving skills improve? Will his gross motor skills develop and catch up? Will he have a growth spurt? Will he understand and choose to have a relationship with God?

Or will Henry fall on the other side of the fence, falling further behind and spending his next 12 years hating school?   Is Henry's future full of friends, schoolwork, and spirituality? Or special education and dependency?

I am constantly waffling on the issue "Is the glass half full or half empty?" I see how strong he is—stronger than I could ever hope to be.   I see the incredible physical obstacles he has already overcome: weighing 1 1/2 lbs. at birth, having underdeveloped lungs, having a grade 3 brain bleed, undergoing heart surgery at under two pounds. And yet by some miracle he has survived!

Still, there are days that I see how far he has to go. He is so small; he struggles with motor skills such as zipping, dressing, cutting with scissors, coloring, running, balancing.   It's the not-knowing that is so hard. There are days when I pick him up and hold him; I look him in the eyes and I want to tell him, "Henry, you're so close.   Work with me; these activities and exercises are all for your benefit. Try a little harder." I always end up crying.   There is a fine line we walk: How much time do we spend coaxing him to practice his writing?   Are we helping him learn life skills....or are we ruining his childhood? He's only a kid once!

Henry and James' immediate future involves starting kindergarten. Sending a child off to his first day of school is one of those momentous days of parenthood.   It is a symbolic "passing of the torch." We parents are telling our children that now it is OK for them to gain a little more independence and to enjoy a new-found freedom. For many parents (usually mothers,

150

but not always) the first day of kindergarten is often harder for them than it is for their children. I think that is how it will be at our house. Catherine tells our friends and family that on that very difficult day they are welcome to come and cry with her. The boys both have attended pre-schools—Henry three different pre-schools in three years; so to them, I think it is going to just be another school.

Parents of muliple-birth children face the decision whether to keep their twins (or triplets) in the same kindergarten class or whether to split them up. Catherine and I went back and forth many times in our decision; it seemed to change daily. Originally we said, "Let's keep them together for kindergarten to help ease the transition into a new school." Eventually we decided to split them up. We came to this decision for a couple of different reasons. James and Henry are very different, and we did not want the teacher to be comparing the two. Henry is an ECSE student with his own IEP and support services; James is not. James is always looking out for his brother, as a big brother would. This is great, but it also means he some times bosses Henry around and tells him what he can and can't do. We made our final decision after we asked the boys separately, away from ear shot, if they wanted to be in the same room with each other next year or in separate rooms. They both answered, "Separate."

As a teacher I have taught twins in both situations, some in separate classrooms and some together. I would say in almost all cases the parents had made the right decision. It really comes down to what is best for each child. There is no right or wrong answer. One cannot simply say all twins must be split up.

At home we practice the 3 Rs: Read, Read, Read. My colleagues who are reading and writing specialists have told me that the research backing up the benefits of reading to our children grows larger every year. Besides reading, the boys paint on their easel in the garage, draw on their wipe boards, solve puzzles, sort and match objects, and practice identifying their ABCs. Both of my sons are also excellent storytellers with vivid imaginations, able to weave multiple characters into their long and winding tales.

The hours upon hours of reading books, singing songs, and telling stories has helped our boys in their love of books and in their imaginary play.

As I watch my sons run around our house, wrestle together on the family room floor, or cuddle together under a blanket with a good book, I realize how fortunate Catherine and I are. The love and joy Henry and James have brought to our family is beyond measure. The problems we face may seem minor to parents who have children with severe disabilities. Many families face worse crises than ours. My blessings go out to them. As parents, Catherine and I have been blessed with two healthy, loving sons.

Of one thing I am certain: in the future, Henry and James will continue to receive from their mother the love and nurturing that is so important to young children. Catherine will be there to play with, sing and read to them. She will be there to wipe away a tear, bandage a scraped knee and laugh at a joke. Most important of all, she will be there to show them unconditional love.

I am confident that our entire family—grandparents, great-grandparents, brothers, sisters, aunts, uncles, and cousins will continue in the future to shower the boys with affection. We have been blessed with a close loving family, and I want my sons to grow up to know just how fortunate they are.

For me these past five years have gone by very quickly. It seems like only yesterday that the boys were born. I want the future to slow down a little so I can keep enjoying the company of my sons before they grow up and move out. Fatherhood is the greatest experience I have ever known. Henry, James, and Catherine have taught me more than I could ever hope to teach them. They have taught me about the unconditional love that is felt between a parent and a child, and between a husband and wife. I have learned how precious and fragile life can be. I have learned what it means to be forgiven. And Henry and James have taught me to believe in miracles.

I look forward to the rest of this journey with my family and know that in the future I will continue to learn from them. Hopefully, we can continue to grow closer together as a family. I have read that the most important factor in a child's development is for him to know that he is loved. Now, after experiencing fatherhood, I know that is true.

Henry, James, and Catherine....
I love you.

Afterward

A year has passed since I presented Catherine with the book *Henry and James: The Miracle of Life*. In that time our sons have attended kindergarten and are now fast approaching their seventh birthday.

Each day during the past school year, Catherine walked both boys up the hill to Groveland Park Elementary School and back home again. The year proved to be a mix of successes and setbacks. James had a great year. By school's end he had met or surpassed all the educational goals for kindergarten; and he developed several friendships. James has moved on to first grade at Groveland School.

Henry's year of kindergarten was more of a struggle. Although there were just 17 students in his class, he was accustomed to being in a smaller class with two or more teachers. In addition, his overall weaknesses in the areas of fine motor skills and processing information (such as following multi-step directions) proved to be too much for him to handle. It was a frustrating year for him and also for us as parents. Even though he had a caring teacher and received support from the special education team—the learning- disabilities teacher, the speech therapist, and the occupational therapist—we all agreed: Henry was not ready for first grade.

Kindergarten is the age when certain learning disabilities start becoming apparent. We still have many more questions than answers when it comes to Henry's academic and cognitive developmental level. He is repeating kindergarten at Como Park Elementary School in a special-needs speech and language-intensive kindergarten/first grade program that was recommended by his specialists at Groveland. Moving Henry to this program would mean he would be attending his fifth school in five years.

After observing the program last spring, both Catherine and I were impressed with its structure: two classroom teachers with Early Childhood Special Education experience and two full-time educational assistants. In addition, three specialists—speech/language clinician, occupational therapist, and physical therapist—all work with the class on a daily basis. Henry can stay with the same educational team for two years. He rides a bus which picks him up and drops him off at our front door.

In April of 2002 the boys were the subject of an article featured on the front page of the Variety section of the *Star Tribune*. The focus of the article was on micro-preemies who have survived and are now of school age. Researchers at the University of Minnesota are starting to map the brains of premature babies as they grow into older childhood. They want to find out if preemies' brains work in similar patterns to those of children who were born at full-term (Cummins, 2002).

The boys are both engaged in activities outside of school. This past summer they finished their fourth set of swimming lessons. They played on a T-ball team and are currently on a soccer team. The boys spent many afternoons in our backyard in their wading pool, spraying each other with the hose.

As a family we enjoyed many activities together during the summer of 2002. We went camping, fishing, and canoeing. The boys took their first portage into the Boundary Waters Canoe Area; James carried the worms and Henry carried a fishing pole. We also spent five days on an island in Lake of the Woods with Catherine's family. Henry loved the speed boat ride out; James was a little scared. Another four days we stayed at a friend's cabin near Lutsen—hiking, fishing, and gazing at the fire. Catherine and I cherish these family outings.

Catherine became involved at the boys' school, volunteering many mornings in their classrooms. She also found a new group of friends—the kindergarten moms of Groveland School. Most importantly, she continued to find ways to shower our boys with love.

157

She remains the rock of support in our house. Her faith in Jesus Christ remains unwavering.

Our family's love for each other continues to grow, and I see more clearly than ever that I have been blessed.

References

Cummins, H. J. "The Littlest Ones," *Star Tribune*, E1 (April 15, 2002).

Miller, K. "Small Miracles," *Star Tribune*, E1 (Mar. 4, 2001).

Slovut, G. "Heart surgery on infant is first of its kind," *Star Tribune*, B3 (Feb. 3, 1996).

(Photo by Sandy Houts)

Jon Westby has been a teacher in the Minneapolis
Public Schools for 14 years. He is currently completing his Master's of Education degree through St.
Mary's University of Winona, Minnesota. In addition to his family, his passions in life are running,
cycling, hiking, and enjoying the great outdoors. He
and his family reside in the Macalester-Groveland
neighborhood of St. Paul, MN.

Copies of this book may be ordered from Kirk House
Publishers: www.kirkhouse.com
Order forms may also be obtained from
the author: jwestby@mpls.k12.mn.us
or the editor: sandrichjh@earthlink.net